FACTORY MAN

FACTORY MAN

How Jim Harbour discovered Toyota's quality and productivity methods and helped the U.S. auto industry get competitive

James E. Harbour
with James V. Higgins

Society of Manufacturing Engineers
Dearborn, Michigan

Library of Congress Control Number: 2008941391
International Standard Book Number (ISBN): 0-87263-860-X
ISBN 13: 978-087263-860-0

Additional copies may be obtained by contacting:
Society of Manufacturing Engineers
Customer Service
One SME Drive, P.O. Box 930
Dearborn, Michigan 48121
1-800-733-4763
www.sme.org/store

SME staff who participated in producing this book:
Rosemary Csizmadia, Senior Production Editor
Steve Bollinger, Manager, Book & Video Publications
Jerome Cook, Cover Concept
Mark Moten, Cover Layout
Frances Kania, Administrative Coordinator

Printed in the United States of America

*This book is dedicated to all the middle-class
workers who toil every day in manufacturing.*

Contents

About the Authors

James E. Harbour is recognized as a leading automotive industry analyst. He has been widely quoted in publications such as *Fortune, Forbes, Newsweek, The New York Times, Washington Post, The Wall Street Journal*, and many others.

In 1980, James Harbour formed Harbour and Associates, Inc., a consulting firm that assists manufacturing companies in improving their overall competitiveness. The firm is dedicated to helping manufacturers develop a strategic focus where the design, product, and manufacturing engineering functions are all focused on continuous improvement of product quality and efficiency. The firm has worked directly with automotive companies throughout the world and has expanded its scope to assist companies in industries such as pharmaceuticals, consumer products, electrical components, furniture, and paper products as they study and apply improvement methods.

Jim Harbour and his team created the first *Harbour Report*, a study of manufacturing performance at original equipment manufacturers (OEMs) in 1980. The report was updated in 1989 and became an annual publication in 1993. The *Harbour Report* is the bible of manufacturing labor efficiency for the automotive industry and has driven massive improvements in manufacturing performance for the OEMs over the last 28 years. Recognized throughout the automotive industry, the report is read by thousands of automotive OEMs, suppliers, financial analysts, and media each year.

Prior to founding Harbour and Associates, Inc., Jim Harbour worked for 28 years in the automotive industry as a manager and director in the manufacturing engineering and financial disciplines for Ford Motor Company and Chrysler Corporation. He retired as head of Harbour and Associates in 1999 and continues to consult with a number of clients.

James V. Higgins covered the worldwide automotive industry for more than 25 years as a reporter, columnist, and editor, primarily for *The Detroit News*.

The recipient of numerous reporting and writing awards, Higgins was named automotive reporter for United Press International in 1979 and joined *The News* in 1981 as its primary auto beat writer. He also served *The News* as business editor, Washington bureau chief, metro editor, and government editor. Higgins left *The News* in May 2006 and has since followed automotive topics as a freelance writer.

Acknowledgments

Over many years, I have been approached by friends and colleagues who said, "Jim, you should write a book about your life in the auto industry and on the factory floor."

I never believed there was enough material to fill a book—until I had lunch one day early in 2008 with a friend, Jim Higgins, a retired business writer from *The Detroit News*. Jim encouraged me to seriously think about telling my story. He reminded me that very few corporate CEOs and government officials really recognize that manufacturing is the foundation this country was built on—creating pride of accomplishment, enormous wealth, and opportunities for the middle class. But I knew that I needed a partner, someone who understood Detroit, the auto industry, manufacturing, and who was, above all, a great writer. Jim agreed to join me in this endeavor. Together we spent endless hours reviewing my years of documentation. Jim spent more endless hours listening to me dump my memory into his tape recorder.

Jim was my choice for several reasons. First, we shared an enthusiasm for the automotive industry and manufacturing, and he was able to jog my memory on specific details. Second, he is focused. Third, he took my drafted copy, chapter after chapter, and made it come alive.

Second, I owe special thanks to Barbara Gaston, my public relations consultant, who kept me focused on my story and how to introduce it to the manufacturing world. She is a great organizer, negotiator, and friend.

I must also thank my wife, Dolores, for the endless hours she spent reading, correcting, and providing her perspective on the many chapters sent to and from Jim's computer. Her rewards were many more dinners at better restaurants and the pleasure of finishing this endeavor.

I also want to thank Tom Stuart, a close friend and retired corporate executive for his valuable input.

To Jim Higgins, Barbara Gaston, my wife, Dolores, and Tom Stuart, I am eternally grateful.

Preface

"MY WAY"

On the factory floor there's no room for bullshit. I spent my life in the heat, stink, and grime of heavy industry, where America earned its bread—and still does, although it's hard to find anybody today who knows it. Let me be blunt about it. I wrote this book because I'm afraid that we'll learn that lesson the hard way. In the autumn of 2008, we were very close to doing just that. America had gone through a 10-year orgy of making money on money. Then came the inevitable crash. Look at history—every financial bubble breaks and we should have seen it coming. At the same time, the nation's domestic automakers—and I'm intimately familiar with them—were also threatened with bankruptcy. So I'm issuing this warning before that falls apart with perhaps even more disastrous long-term consequences for the nation.

Henry Ford said that hard times are caused by the mistakes we make when times are good. This applies to the nation's manufacturing crisis as well as its sub-prime mortgage bubble. Sugar coating is definitely not my way. I know precisely what mistakes were made in Detroit and you'll read about them here. Hell, for a long time I was part of the problem. But now it's time to ask yourself: what's real? Where did the wealth come from that was so outrageously compounded through weird financial instruments by bankers and brokers who must have been totally out of touch with everyday American life? I'm no economist, but I'd bet that most of it had a common foundation—the wages of people in manufacturing who make things that people want to buy.

Old Henry also said that a manufacturing company is in deep trouble when it starts paying more attention to its money investments than its factories. I think we've seen that this also applies to America as a manufacturing nation. Ford taught the world, that in a competitive business, whoever runs his factories best is going to win in the end. I can personally vouch for that. When a factory is neglected by its management, productivity and quality suffer—and somebody could be badly injured. When an entire industry does the same, it gets stomped into the ground by people who have kept an eye on that production line. When Ford won, by creating the most powerful manufacturing system ever seen, he transformed the world and made America rich. Then came the stock market bubble, the Great Depression with suffering all around, and war. Right after World War II we were just about the only manufacturing economy in the world that hadn't been flattened by bombs, and it didn't matter how we ran our factories. Even after Japan's auto industry was up and running, the competitive threat was ignored. We got fatter than ever.

This is where I came in. The story of American industry in the last 60 years is my story. My family, rooted in the factory life, was scarred by the sting and humiliation of the Depression. But the war and its prosperous aftermath rescued us. After an enlistment in the U.S. Navy—where I got my first hard lessons in discipline, teamwork, and leadership—I went to work on a Detroit assembly line. Then came schooling, and I stepped hopefully onto one of America's greatest career paths in the early postwar years—a salaried job in the auto industry. As a factory floor analyst, productivity manager, and manufacturing executive at the former Chrysler Corp., I watched day by day as the system that Ford built began to rot. Some of us protested: we saw the crap going out the door. But upper management didn't want to listen. There was a big party going on. It was the Golden Age of the auto industry, and it lasted more than three decades after the war. When it finally ended, no one who had been wrestling with the problems of factory production was surprised. In particular, Detroit's collapse came as no shock to the few of us who had begun to pay attention to the rise of the auto industry in Japan.

When Chrysler fell, so did I. But the day after I was shown the door, a job jumped into my lap that changed things forever—not just for me, I believe, but for the U.S. auto industry overall. I became part of a small, private consulting team that was given unprecedented access to Toyota's factory system. Later, I gathered what I had learned into the first *Harbour Report*, which set Detroit on its ear by publicly exposing for the first time how inefficient the Big Three had become compared with the Japanese.

Detroit's response at first was anger and denial. How can that tinny, boxy, pitiful little Corolla® make any difference in the land of Cadillac Coupe de Villes and Buick Roadmasters? I became the enemy. The Big Three beat me up pretty badly and I have the scars to prove it. But we persisted, and the *Harbour Report* soon became what it is today—the auto industry's annual gut-check of manufacturing efficiency. I believe these studies helped prod U.S.-based manufacturers to make huge gains in quality and efficiency, and not only in the auto industry. Warner-Lambert, the pharmaceutical and consumer products giant, was one of our greatest success stories.

But the Detroit-based automakers haven't gone far enough, and now they're running out of time. *Why should anybody care?*

For one thing, we've already lost entire industries. Here's just one example. Since 1980, the Detroit automakers have spent billions of dollars buying large stamping presses to make car bodies more efficiently. Virtually all of that money went to companies in Europe and Japan. Among auto industry supplier companies, proud, historic names have disappeared. Budd Co., which invented the modern welded car body, is gone. Companies of equal stature are bankrupt—Dana Corp., which made car frames and other parts, and the diverse auto industry supplier Delphi Automotive Systems, to name just two among dozens.

When the big names on Wall Street began to topple, so many Detroit companies were being reorganized under Chapter 11 of the U.S. Bankruptcy Code that a morbid joke ran the rounds—"They'll have to start holding bankruptcy court in tents." Then General Motors Corp. canceled health insurance for its salaried retirees who had become eligible for Medicare. This was just the latest in a long series of wage and benefit cuts by the Detroit-based automakers and their suppliers. In other words, the wealth that Henry Ford helped to create is evaporating.

You might think that America would get along fine without GM, Ford, and Chrysler as long as Toyota, Honda, and Nissan are here, but I'm not willing to risk it. It isn't just manufacturing jobs that are at stake—and if GM, Ford, and Chrysler fail, you won't believe the bloodbath. The nation's overall manufacturing competence will be at risk when the basics of automotive design and engineering are transferred to Japan, Korea, and China. But this doesn't have to be. I've worked for 30 years to prevent that, and if my story will do something to head that off, then I've got to tell it.

Chapter 1
A Toolmaker's Son

*"There is one rule for the industrialist and that is: Make the best
quality of goods possible at the lowest cost possible,
paying the highest wages possible."*

"Quality means doing it right when no one is looking."
—*Henry Ford*

I grew up during the Great Depression, when life for factory
men and their families had turned hellish. I was born in my
grandmother's house in Manchester, New Hampshire, in 1927.
My father, a French-Canadian, was a tool and die maker in the
shoe industry. My mother was Polish, from Manitowoc, Wisconsin.
They were fighters; they had a tough time agreeing on anything in
their very challenging lives. Manchester was a factory town with
woolen mills in addition to the shoe industry. It had been prosperous, but now was dying because of foreign competition. The woolen
mills were going to Japan, and shoe manufacturers were moving
to Italy. So my father went to look for work in the auto industry,
where tool and die makers were at the top of the blue-collar food
chain. They made the huge dies used to stamp out fenders, doors,
hoods, bumpers, and other car body parts.

We ended up in a one-bedroom house in Ecorse, Michigan, a
suburb along the Detroit River just south of the city. With Canada
in view across the river, Ecorse had been a big bootlegging town
during Prohibition with speakeasies lining the riverbank. But
when we got there it was a miniature Pittsburgh, with two steel
mills belching smoke and tinting the night sky pink from the hot
iron. The massive Ford Rouge, the world's biggest industrial complex at the time, was about 10 miles to the northwest. My father
went to work at the Rouge, but was laid off as the Depression

took hold. We were a family of three kids in a one-bedroom house. I slept in the bathtub, my sister on the floor, and my brother in a dresser drawer. And we had to take a bath once a week, if we needed it or not.

Our house was one block from the railroad tracks. I remember that every day we'd go down to the railroad tracks and throw rocks at the open coal cars that were passing by. If we could knock some coal loose, we'd take it home to run the heating system. One day the coal train stopped right in front of our house. I couldn't believe my luck. It had never stopped before, and I don't know why it did this time, but it was a golden opportunity. The cars were full, so I climbed up on the hopper car and started throwing coal over the side. All of a sudden the train started moving! Here I was, headed south! It gathered speed and kept going for miles and miles. We went through the city of Trenton, which had always seemed to me about as far away as China. Finally the train slowed down and I was able to jump off. I was in Rockwood, at least 15 miles from home, and I didn't know how to get back except for following the tracks. I finally got home about 9:30 or 10:00 that night and there was my dad with a wagon, picking up the coal.

In the winter, my father would go downtown to shovel snow. That was the only job he could get. They'd shovel the snow into trucks and dump it into the Detroit River.

But slowly the Depression subsided, and we moved to a larger home on Detroit's west side. I went to Cooley High School, which had nearly 4,000 students. The freshmen and sophomores went to school from noon to 4 p.m., and the juniors and seniors from 8 a.m. to noon. The same teachers worked both shifts—try that today! For a while I spent my afternoons playing basketball, but soon I had to go to work. The family needed money more than I needed basketball.

We had a family ritual that, in retrospect, was my first lesson in quality. After dinner on the first Sunday of every month, my father would give my brother and me a haircut. He used a pair of those old hand-operated clippers and some scissors, and I hated the damn things because he never sharpened them. He was a highly skilled tool and die maker; but these were two tools that he didn't maintain properly. They yanked out more hair than they cut, and I would yell, "Dad, you're pulling!"

I especially remember when this dreaded ritual took place on December 7, 1941, two weeks away from my 14th birthday. We headed down to the basement for the haircut, but soon we heard my mother calling, "Dad, come up." The Japanese had just attacked Pearl Harbor. So the ritual ended, and I never got another haircut in the basement. With the war on, my Dad immediately got a job in St. Louis making dies for airplane wings. Thereafter we got 50 cents for haircuts every month.

When my 16th birthday arrived in December, 1943, I asked Dad for permission to join the Navy. "Hell no," he said. But a year later he relented, because he knew I didn't want to take my chances with the draft when I turned 18. So I joined up, and was shipped off to the Great Lakes Naval Training Camp near Chicago with 119 other teenaged recruits.

A Marine drill sergeant was our new leader, the kind of guy I'd later find managing some of the auto plants where I worked. He was a huge, compelling man with a deep commanding voice. He firmly stated his orders and expectations for our daily training, with the result that the next three months were hell on earth: Out of your bunk at 6 a.m., a 15-minute breakfast, five hours of nonstop drills, a 15-minute lunch, and five more painful hours until you thought you would collapse except that you were terrified of what might happen if you gave in to that thought. Dinner was a blessed half-hour. Then there

Figure 1-1. Jim Harbour, age 18, U.S. Navy, San Francisco, California.

was more drilling, running, and marching, sometimes with heavy backpacks, until you prayed for lights out at 10 p.m. A dozen or so recruits tried to bail out, claiming everything from fatigue to homesickness. But this Marine was having none of it, even though his boss—a Navy lieutenant—suggested he back off. Today I can see that his focus, in essence, was on quality. He was the best—the *very* best—and after 120 days of this we thought we were the best, too. And so did some commanders at the Great Lakes Station, because we were chosen out of 20 training companies to march in a downtown Chicago parade.

For three months the Navy tested us to see what job we were best qualified for after boot camp. I was shocked and devastated when they told me my future was to be a cook. That was *not* what I signed up for, but off I went to cook school, and to the prospect of a dreary and undistinguished military career. As the lowest ranking sailor in the galley, I had to get up at 4:30 a.m. and peel two tons of potatoes. I used a peeling machine, which was like a clothes dryer lined with sandpaper. It took off the skins, but I had to remove the eyes by hand. Or maybe there were two tons of oranges waiting to be peeled; you dump them in hot water and the skin practically falls off. I made several visits to the base personnel office asking for a re-evaluation, but those requests fell on deaf ears.

Then one Saturday morning when all the higher-ranking galley crew members were on weekend leave, I was assigned to the admiral's mess. The admiral, noting I was new, firmly asked me how I liked the Navy, cook school, and the Great Lakes Training Center. It hit me immediately that this was my last chance for salvation. "Sir, I hate cook school and I hate being at Great Lakes," I told him. "I joined up to go to sea with the *real* Navy." Later in life I learned that speaking up bluntly doesn't always get you what you want, and might backfire. But this time it worked. It was my first chance to do it "my way." Within 72 hours, I was reassigned to the Pacific Fleet. My next stop was San Francisco, where I boarded a troop ship for Hawaii. I was retested for a new assignment, which turned out to be finance school. What a life—three months on Oahu while learning the principles of accounting!

While at finance school, I again applied for what I thought would be a more interesting assignment—as a deep-sea diver. My God, I was accepted! And I didn't mind the Navy's main reason for taking me—not because I was physically powerful and daring, but because I had two years of welding training at a trade school co-sponsored by Cooley High School in Detroit. So I enjoyed another three months in Pearl Harbor taking basic diver training. But the Navy abruptly cancelled the diving program since the war was now over and there was a surplus of skilled divers.

My first sea assignment was on the U.S.S. Palmyra, the Navy's only available ship that could support hardhat, deep-sea divers. We were headed for Bikini Atoll to participate in Operation Crossroads, an exercise to test the impact of an atomic blast on a fleet of some 90 ships. It was stunning to see the mass of doomed warships, including the U.S. battleship Arkansas, the Japanese battleship Nagato, the U.S. aircraft carrier Saratoga, and the German pocket battleship Prince Eugen. Two bombs were dropped, Able and Baker. The Palmyra's assignment was to speed back into the bomb blast area and re-moor any ship that had broken loose from its buoy. Then our diving crews were to assess the damage on the 21 ships that sank, and attempt to raise some of the smaller vessels. We left Bikini in late 1946, and after a thorough cleaning to get rid of any lingering radiation, the Palmyra was decommissioned early in 1947 in Texas.

I was reassigned to other ships and finally to the U.S.S. Mercury AK 20, a cargo ship that every six weeks made a round trip from Norfolk, Virginia to Argencia, Newfoundland, to Plymouth, England, to Bremerhaven, Germany, and then back home. I was on my last voyage in November, 1948 when we were caught in a hurricane about 200 miles east of Puerto Rico. The empty ship was riding high in the water, not the best way to take on a storm. About 5 a.m. at the height of the storm, with the wind behind the fantail, the ship started to split in half. The bow of the vessel began to sink, and we desperately tried to keep it afloat by lashing cables to the bow and winching them tight to the superstructure. In this situation we floated perilously for two days, wearing life jackets the entire time. Finally, the bow sank and a 120-foot tug arrived and towed us back to Norfolk. We were a sorry sight, and every ship we passed as we entered port got a laugh at our expense. But when the voyage ended, my discharge was finalized and I could go home. I loved the Navy—the tropics, liberty at overseas ports and, yes, even the rough seas. But it was time to get busy with my career.

When I got home in December, 1948, I was determined to get two things: an education and a job. Since I had attended the Navy's Finance School, the logical step was to go to college for a finance degree. Growing up in the heart of industry, I was also determined to learn how factories worked. At this time the auto industry was just beginning to pull out of its wartime mode, when Detroit had earned its reputation as the arsenal of democracy. Americans did without new automobiles during the war years, and the automobile industry was racing to participate in the great seller's market in cars and light trucks that marked the immediate postwar years. But the only job I could get right away was as an hourly production worker at the old Chrysler Jefferson Avenue assembly plant. "Antique" is probably a better word than "old" to describe the plant, which dated from the earliest days of the auto industry and at one time had built Maxwells.

I would get up in the morning and catch the streetcar to my classes at The Business Institute. Then I'd board the streetcar again to downtown Detroit, where I'd transfer to another car for the ride out East Jefferson to the plant. I worked the afternoon shift from 3 p.m. to 11:30 p.m. My first job was as a dues-paying member of the United Automobile, Aerospace, and Agricultural Implement Workers of America (UAW). I worked in "body in white," which is the auto industry's jargon for the production stage in which the car body's unpainted sheet metal (including doors, hoods, and deck lids) has been assembled, but before the components (chassis, engine, transmission, suspensions) and trim (windshields, seats, upholstery, electrical equipment, etc.) have been added. It was punishing. I'd lift body panels off of a conveyer line and place them on a "buck," a fixture that held different panels together while they were welded. We had to wrap rags around our bleeding hands to protect them from the sharp edges of the stamped metal. The company wouldn't buy you gloves, and at that time the UAW wasn't pressing management to issue them. When the bucks were loaded, along would come some higher-paid workers who did all the welding, wrestling these big, heavy electric welding guns into position to make thousands of welds per day. When they were finished with a body they'd send it along to the paint shop. It was a hell of a job.

Around midnight every night I'd take the streetcar home. But this routine varied quite a bit in July, August, and September. Whenever the temperature hit 80° F (27° C) or higher it would get really hot inside the plant on the afternoon shift and the union would call us out. We would just walk off the job. It was 1949, the UAW had won some tough organizing battles at each of the Detroit automakers and now was flexing its muscle. I don't know that the day shift ever walked out because of hot weather, but on the afternoon shift we always did. Then would come October and November and we'd work pretty steadily. The union couldn't care less about stopping the line. America was desperate for new cars, and the plant was focused entirely on output. Productivity was not an issue, nor was quality.

After 15 months of this, I graduated from business school, and decided to leave factory life behind. The next two years I spent in the mortgage business. But the less said about this the better—it was another job I learned to hate.

In 1952, Detroit was still booming, and so I got an interview for a job as a financial analyst at Ford Motor Company's Highland Park Assembly Plant—the legendary home of the Model T® and the birthplace of modern mass production. To my great surprise, they hired me on the spot.

Chapter 2

My Factory Education

"If you do it right 51 percent of the time you will end up a hero."
—*Alfred P. Sloan, CEO of General Motors Corp., 1923–1946*

"We let our quality go bad. We got careless;
we got sloppy; we built lousy quality cars."
—*Henry Ford II, Ford Motor Co. CEO, 1960–1979*

Ford's Highland Park plant reeked with history. The modern industrial assembly line actually had been designed in an earlier Ford plant on Piquette Avenue a few miles to the east. But at Highland Park, the system was honed to incredible efficiency by a team of absolute factory geniuses. The price of the Model T® kept dropping until just about everyone could afford one.

Highland Park was also the birthplace of the blue-collar middle class. In January, 1914 Henry Ford startled Detroit and the world by announcing he would pay some unskilled assemblers the dream sum of $5 per day. Henry wasn't naturally generous. The work was so hard that the company had to hire something like 40,000 workers a year to fill 10,000 production jobs. People couldn't take the pace, but the premium pay was a strong incentive. Myself, I was ecstatic when they told me I'd earn $300 a month as a financial analyst in 1952. Imagine that, $1.80 per hour!

The place was huge, floor after floor of manufacturing space under six independent plant managers. The facility made light-duty trucks, farm tractors, interior trim, paint, artificial leather, and 2.75-inch bazooka rockets for the U.S. Army. Ford hadn't forgotten about efficiency. In 1952, it was still under the tutelage of the famed "whiz kids," the team of Army efficiency experts brought to Dearborn right after World War II by young Henry Ford II.

One of the kids, the future Defense Secretary Bob McNamara, was head of Ford Division and also managed the Highland Park complex. Focused on productivity, my job was to roam the shop floor, looking for ways to reduce labor and overhead costs. The official goal was to improve productivity by 3 percent every year to cover the costs of annual UAW wage increases, while cutting overhead costs by 6 percent per year. Later I learned that 10–15 percent annual improvements would have been more like it and achievable, but the job was to meet the 3 percent budget and keep the division executives off your back. At the same time, we were under a corporate dictate to cut salaried headcount by 10 percent per year. Survival was a challenge.

I would spend my lunch hours studying how trucks and tractors were built. I chatted with fellow workers and supervisors about their jobs as often as I could. Gradually, it dawned on me that a big change in the executive pecking order had taken place over time. Manufacturing executives used to rule Ford, but now their power was slipping away. They had no input into the design of the parts or components they were supposed to make. It didn't matter if the thing couldn't be made with quality or productivity; the dictate was "make it anyway." This was the beginning of an operating system that later became notorious in Detroit. The various disciplines involved in car manufacturing were walled off from each other. The product engineer would toss his finished design over a wall, where it bonked a startled manufacturing engineer right on the head and started a scramble to find a way to build it.

At Highland Park, however, I was doing my own fabricating. All Ford plants and offices at that time had a suggestion system. It wasn't very productive, because when a good idea came along, managers often would claim that they thought it up. One day, I was watching a team of hourly workers struggling to put together an interior truck door panel that was made of four separate hardboard pieces. Getting a good fit was nearly impossible. Finally I took the four pieces home, bought a large piece of hardboard, and cut a single sheet in the shape of the four-piece assembly. The stubborn product engineers eventually bought the new design, but I was told it couldn't be entered in the suggestion program because it was my job to figure out cost and productivity improvements like that. But four months later, I was called into the plant manager's office and handed a check for $3,000—the top prize in the suggestion derby. That was a tidy sum in the summer of 1956. My-oh-my, did we celebrate when I got home!

The triumph didn't last, though. I survived the 10 percent annual cut for four years. Then, on a Friday afternoon in April of my fifth year, it bit me in the ass. My boss, the manager of the trim plant, called me in and told me I had no future at Ford because I didn't have a four-year college degree. Throughout those five years at Highland Park I had been attending night school at

Figure 2-1. Jim Harbour receives $3,000 award from Ford Motor Company for his cost-saving idea—fabricating interior truck door panels.

Wayne State University studying finance and engineering. But I still was short of credits to graduate. Well, with four kids at home, I had a month to get on another payroll before things got too tight. So, I drove the three blocks over to Chrysler Corp. headquarters, also in Highland Park. Behold, they hired me right away at $600 a month! I almost couldn't believe my luck; now I was up to the incredible sum of $3.60 per hour.

I was assigned to the Forge & Foundry Division as a budget analyst. This was the bedrock of automobile manufacturing. There were four foundries, where metal was melted into castings, and two forge plants, where parts were hammered into shape in a giant automated version of the old blacksmith at his anvil. All the plant managers had come up from the bottom. They were hard-working, tough-talking, brute-force managers who personally knew how to operate all the machinery in the plant. Nobody had a college degree. At first I worked on the division central staff—a desk job that I didn't particularly like. But after four months, I was made budget supervisor at the Detroit Forge plant. Despite the title, I was a floor analyst and I spent all of my time on the plant floor. It was fun.

The plant manager was a guy named Chuck Mote. For about 80 percent of his day, you would see him, barrel-chested, stalking the plant floor, showing people how to run a hammer or press. I didn't know much about Chrysler Corp. at the time, its focus, or goals, or even that much about its cars. The only thing that interested me was learning what made a plant successful. The plant made engine crankshafts, connecting rods, torsion bars for suspension systems, and a lot more. It was awesome to watch people heat a 120-lb (54-kg) piece of steel to 2,200° F (1,204° C), roll it into a forging press, and make it come out like a crankshaft. The focus was entirely on output. Machine operators were paid on a piecework basis, and they got paid even if the part was defective and had to be scrapped. The plant had a metallurgist who tried to guarantee that the incoming steel was good, but all he could do was perform a few simple tests. The engine plants that machined our crankshafts and connecting rods would often send back the parts that had been scrapped. Our response was to boost production to cover the scrap rate, not to try and find out what was going wrong. We had no statistical analysis and no process control. Our only quality assurance plan was to try to maintain forging dies and hammers to a minimum standard, but this was obviously not working very well. But we had visited similar plants at General Motors and Ford, and we knew they weren't doing any better.

And we were filthy. This was thought to be the normal by-product of a hot, dirty manufacturing process. We had a huge staff of janitors continually trying to clean up. Later, when I went to Japan and visited Toyota's foundries and forges, I literally could not believe my eyes. They were as clean as a whistle. They didn't live with dirt and slime, and had created methods to keep their foundries clean. Sure, dirt and dust would accumulate temporarily, but it wasn't left to pile up shift after shift. This was a powerful revelation. After visiting Toyota, I promised myself that in the future I would question everything and accept nothing about a manufacturing process as inevitable or inherently factual.

On April Fool's Day, 1959, I was promoted to controller of the New Castle, Indiana Forge Plant. New Castle was a town of about 9,000 people that Chrysler had adopted. The company was so profitable that it had helped build the high school, which bore its name. When it needed a new gym, Chrysler helped organize a fund drive to build a structure big enough to practically seat the entire town. And nearly everybody would go there on a basketball night. When there was a varsity game, you could have walked into almost any house in town and robbed it blind.

We made a host of forgings such as steering knuckles, ball joints, transmission shafts, and so forth. It was a treat for me, because the plant that machined these parts into their final form was right next door. I would go over there and watch the machining process to see if we were making a halfway decent part. If we were producing scrap because of a bad die or press or faulty material, the foreman would scream; but again, there were no real controls over repair or scrap rates. I was beginning to understand that the entire corporation had the same problem. There was always a rush to fix a shop-floor problem, but never did anyone try to identify and fix its root cause. For every thousand parts made, there might be only 900 good ones, and the scrap bill was out of sight. We finally convinced management to set up a number of teams to analyze the problems with six major products. Each team had an engineer, a quality analyst, machining and forging plant supervisors, a financial analyst, and two hourly workers. After weeks of meetings and data collection, we finally identified the major causes of our 15.6 percent scrap rate for steering knuckles:

- cracked forgings, 37 percent;
- heat-treating problems, 24 percent;
- machining problems, 21 percent; and
- defective steel, 18 percent.

The forging plant manager was not happy, to say the least, that 79 percent of the problems came from his factory. We were the culprit and had to respond. So we set up teams to address defective steel, ineffective heat treating, and cracked forgings. Four months later, we published our results: the scrap rate had been reduced to 8.8 percent, mostly because the metallurgists and purchasing guys had been able to get better steel coming into the plant. It was called a victory, even though the scrap rate at 8.8 percent today would be considered atrocious. Later, I found that Toyota operated with a scrap rate below 0.5 percent.

I'm not sure if I was personally making a good impression on my bosses at the time. I was constantly being criticized. "Don't spend so much time on the plant floor," they said. "Your job's in the office." But in the fall of 1961, I got another promotion—this time as controller of the Indianapolis plant. Here they made three-speed automatic transmissions and steering gears, and the plant had been recently retooled to make the auto industry's first alternator, which replaced the old electric generator. Starters and distributors were also made, all-new products on all-new machinery.

The Indianapolis plant was heaven after working in a forging plant. The machining and assembly lines were clean, and the plant had a huge staff of young and aggressive supervisors, engineers, and analysts. But it was fighting a major quality problem, and a productivity nightmare. Every alternator, distributor, and starter was 100 percent tested, and the results were horrible. Failure rates were enormous. The vehicle assembly plants were always running out of product because we were filling the scrap heap faster than we were filling the shipping containers. The plant was putting in thousands of hours of overtime, with two 10-hour daily shifts including Saturdays and Sundays, to try to keep up with demand. Every week some vice president or executive vice president stormed into the plant demanding: "What's wrong and when will it be fixed? Why do you have so many people? Why are you working so much overtime?" Never mind that the product engineers were making an average of five engineering changes per week for each product; the top executives said it was a manufacturing problem and we'd better fix it. With a corporate officer down your throat every minute, it was hard to get any work done.

So we finally adopted the team approach that had worked at New Castle. Reject rates had been 27 percent for alternators, 23 percent for starters, and 18 percent for distributors. To tackle this, we had to look at supplier quality, tooling and plant processing problems, staffing levels, repair and rework rates, quality standards, and the need for overtime. Each team eventually laid out a detailed plan for recovery.

The teams included the brilliant hotshots from the plant superintendent and quality manager's offices, but also several key foremen and a great group of hourly workers who emerged as heroes, even though they did themselves out of a lot of overtime. Purchasing people were enlisted to improve supplier quality. They were reluctant to leave their nice corporate offices, but eventually delivered. The tooling suppliers spent hours resetting and rebuilding their machines. Instead of fighting like cats and dogs, the production superintendent and quality control manager began to work together. Astonishingly, the hoity-toity product engineers from Highland Park came down and helped. We could only guess that some senior vice president had kicked them out of their offices and forced them to make the trip to Indianapolis to see what was happening in the real world.

It took about a year, but we cut the workforce hours in half and reduced defects by about 90 percent. Even so, we were not the best manufacturer around for this kind of product.

It was an interesting job—lots of fun trying to turn a plant around. But it was time to move up again. In February, 1963, I was made controller of the Trenton Engine Plant located about 20 miles south of Detroit. There I worked for a guy named Jim Cypher, a 6-ft-5-in. (196-cm), 240-lb (109-kg) ex-Marine who had fought on Iwo Jima. He was just like my drill sergeant at Great Lakes, a huge, passionate, dedicated manager. The guy took no prisoners. One day he had a sign erected outside that said Trenton builds the "World's Finest Engines." We did not build the world's finest engines. The sign was really meant to inspire the workforce, which was one of the most important in Chrysler's factory system. The plant made the six-cylinder, L-head engine, the 383-in.^{3} V8, and the 427-in.^{3} hemi-head engine. Richard Petty ran our hemi in NASCAR®, winning race after race and tying his name to Chrysler forever.

For us at the plant, the quality of the engines was always in question. Machining of cylinder bores was so inaccurate that we'd have to measure every bore and select one of 12 or 13 different piston sizes to fit. Later we would be matched against competitors who had one piston size for an engine, or maybe two. We did the same for connecting rods and crankshafts—we couldn't machine a crankshaft right. So we would purchase several sizes of main bearings for the crankshafts, ±.001 in. (±0.03 mm), to guarantee they'd work. It was almost back to the old days of craft production when every piece of a rifle was fitted separately by a skilled worker and there were no interchangeable parts. At Trenton, nobody talked about a gap of .04 or .08 in. (1 or 2 mm) in an engine component. If it measured within .2 in. (5 mm), which is a difference easily visible to the naked eye, that was okay. Our piston plant in Etobicoke, Ontario made pistons by the thousands and we'd machine them in various sizes. Again there were tons of scrap; and again nobody ever tried to solve the cause of the problem that made us machine and use different sizes of pistons or main bearings instead of just one size. It never came up.

I approached Cypher, the plant manager, and suggested we start a process of addressing the quality and cost problems. Since these problems cut across every engine made at the plant, we agreed to start with the largest production engine, the straight (or inline) six cylinder. In effect, we were doing what later became a cardinal rule of quality improvement: don't try to eat the whole elephant, just take a bite at a time. The six-cylinder engine problems included:

- high amounts of foundry scrap for cylinder blocks and heads;
- high amounts of piston scrap;
- an out-of-control honing process (*honing* is a machining operation that shapes the cylinder bore to the correct size);
- out-of-control camshaft and crankshaft honing processes; and
- the plant was forced to stock various main bearing sizes that could mate with any oversized or undersized crankshaft because of the lack of process control.

We both agreed that this required a team approach. But he said that, if we were to form teams, we would have to include as many hourly workers as salaried staff because hourly workers knew as well as anyone why we were consistently producing parts that had to be scrapped or repaired. This sounded like my Marine drill sergeant at Great Lakes Naval Training Station, who demanded that all recruits function as one team.

Over time—and I mean months—the teams of salaried engineers and blue-collar workers gathered a ton of statistics that allowed them to focus on the major problems. But solving the causes of the problems wasn't so simple. First, the foundry had to improve its processes. That eventually happened, which reduced the number of defective cylinder blocks and heads from over 6 percent of output to less than 3 percent. Maintenance personnel and tooling engineers gradually improved the capability of cylinder boring and honing operations as well as the crankshaft main bearing honing process. So we were able to reduce the number of unique piston sizes from 13 to four and unique main bearing sizes from six to three. This was a monumental achievement in those days, but I would learn later from Toyota that it should have been only the start. Despite some good work, the team process died after our quality and engineering workforce got buried in other major plant expansion projects.

Undoubtedly the biggest problem we had in our U.S. manufacturing plants in the 1960s was a lack of statistical quality training. We had no statistical process control (SPC), where machine operators regularly check the dimensions of the parts they're producing so they'll know instantly if things are getting out of control. SPC later became one of the main tools used in factory operations to analyze problems. Auto factories of that era focused on the kind of statistics that Wall Street could understand, like profit and cash flow, and not so much on the kind of engineering statistics that might have been used to boost quality and keep customers happy.

I'd like to say that we worked wonders at Trenton, as we had done at New Castle and Indianapolis. I can't, but at least I was able to move on after two years. When you're coming up as a manager in the auto industry, especially in manufacturing, you have to move around a lot and get used to it. So late in 1964, I headed down to Dayton, Ohio as controller of Chrysler's Airtemp Division.

The division had an interesting history. When Walter P. Chrysler built the Chrysler Building in New York, he wanted it to be the world's first air-conditioned office tower. So, in the grand fashion of the auto barons of his day, he formed a company to make large commercial air conditioners. When I got to Airtemp, they were making a lot of additional products: car air conditioners, heaters, radiators, evaporators, and condenser coils. Heaters were the biggest automotive product. People at that time weren't yet ready to buy cars equipped with air conditioners when you could just open the windows. At one time, it was thought that air conditioning wouldn't work in buildings that had windows. I had been hired by the division president in Detroit, so imagine my surprise when I got to Dayton for the first time and discovered that the buildings didn't have windows—they were air conditioned.

Airtemp was a self-contained business unit, so this would be my introduction to sales and marketing operations, dealers, and pricing decisions. One thing was a real treat. The product engineers were in the same building as the manufacturing engineers. You could actually go over and talk to the people designing the products and offer them some input. It wasn't that we had a lot of influence, but at least you could get in a suggestion now and then. Nevertheless, many of the problems were familiar. There were substantial amounts of scrap and rework, but nobody paid attention unless the defect rate exceeded double digits. We had little commonality of parts and a great deal of complexity. I found it was nearly impossible to accurately gauge production costs, piece by piece. Ultimately we installed the latest IBM central computer system to track manufacturing costs, but it took two years to develop the systems that gave us an accurate picture.

There was heavy competition with some great companies: General Electric, Whirlpool, Carrier, and Trane. But the division was making a lot of money. When Chrysler corporate staff officials came down to visit us, they always had one question: "What product line is the most profitable, car air conditioning or commercial?"

The answer always went back from the president: "Commercial." It was a big line of baloney. Chrysler's focus was automotive, and we probably shouldn't have been in these other commercial businesses, but our president wasn't about to tell them anything else. It was obvious he wanted to stay in the commercial field despite everything, and he and I soon clashed.

Internal studies clearly reflected that the commercial air conditioning business was a big loser. List prices meant nothing. Room air-conditioner prices were controlled by the giant retailers. Whole-house units, as well as furnaces, were sold to home builders at giveaway prices. The only way you could get an order to build a large, commercial air-conditioning system was if an architect specified your product, and they usually specified Trane and Carrier. I got on the wrong side of my boss when I pointed all this out, and this hastened my next move. Even though it was a loser, we got approval to build a new plant in Bowling Green, Kentucky to make commercial systems. It soon fell apart. Some time after I left Dayton, the commercial part of the business was sold, and the Bowling Green plant is now home of the Chevrolet Corvette®.

I had now spent 15 years in the heart of manufacturing, and I had learned a lot. I have to confess that I had largely bought into a system where everybody, from the head office to the customer, expected that a new car or truck would have a given number of defects. Remember the lemons . . . the cars that couldn't be fixed? We made them. It was simple to do. Somebody missed a weld on the assembly line, and the car had a squeak or rattle that the dealer couldn't even find—much less fix. But I had seen what can happen when you try to get at the cause of a problem, which is a matter of changing systems instead of practices. I had seen what a night-and-day difference it could make if design and manufacturing people just talked to each other. And I was ready to try to put those lessons into effect on a larger stage when the call finally came.

Chapter 3

The Chrysler Debacle

"There are very few people who don't know what the Olds 88 is. It has always been in the same position and in the same price class. But at Chrysler we have had so much interruption in continuity of size, name, and styles that customers didn't know what the Dodge 440 was or what the Plymouth Fury was—and they couldn't be assured that they would still be there next year.

"Detroit always has been referred to as the automotive capital of the United States, but more and more of us in the industry are coming to realize this city is much more than that. It is also the automotive capital of the world. Fast as demand for motor vehicles in the United States has grown during the past 10 or 15 years, the demand in the rest of the world has grown even faster. And in those 10 or 15 years, every company in the industry has been moving out into the rest of the world, investing in facilities for production and distribution on six continents to be in a position to participate in the continued healthy growth of the world market."
—Lynn Townsend, Chrysler chairman

The destruction of Chrysler Corp. took place right before my eyes. I played a key, if unwilling, role in it. We were inefficient. We made defective cars. But Ford and GM were in the same boat. Chrysler was making money despite that.

When I joined the central office staff in 1968, a big change was about to take place—the heavy government regulation of the auto industry. Safety rules, clean-air regulations, and finally the onerous Corporate Average Fuel Economy (CAFÉ) Law dictated improvements in gas mileage across the entire vehicle lineup. General Motors had become so dominant in the market that it could control pricing. In effect, Chrysler survived at GM's mercy. If the No. 1 automaker held prices at a certain level, Chrysler could struggle to keep cash and profits flowing. GM, thankfully, was watchful about pricing the competition out of business, because the government anti-trust regulators were always on its back.

The era of regulation sounded a new note. The bill to meet engineering standards was immense, but the government wouldn't let the Big Three cooperate on the radical, top-to-bottom vehicle and factory redesigns that would be necessary. For every automaker it would cost about the same amount to hire engineers and get the work done. But GM could spread those costs over three times as many vehicle sales as Chrysler. If you added in the rise of foreign competition at this time, it smelled just like bankruptcy. Sadly, the management team that took over Chrysler in the early 1960s didn't quite see it that way. Their prescription was to try to boost sales and revenue overseas. Foreign markets were growing. Ford and GM had been international companies for decades and were in a good position to tap that growth, but Chrysler was almost exclusively tied to North America. Fortunately, the domestic market was also growing—it was the Golden Age, remember—and Chrysler had some cash in the till. It was promptly squandered in a poorly conceived international expansion drive. When the company assigned me to the audit staff at headquarters in Highland Park, I soon found myself right in the middle of that mess.

Auditing, yuck! This was something done by CPAs, bean counters. Audits, I had always believed, were dense and opaque financial documents. So when they asked me to be the head of an international audit team, at first I choked. But it was then made clear to me that these were to be operational, not financial reviews. I was expected to manage a team that evaluated all the manufacturing and engineering operations in the new international unit. This was a big, and welcome, change from what I had expected. Once again I could get my hands dirty on the plant floor.

Chrysler had a major conflict of interest scandal in the late 1950s. Its company president, William C. Newberg, was accused of owning stock in two companies that supplied parts to Chrysler, without disclosing those interests to the board of directors. He was publicly disgraced and broomed. His replacement, Lester L. "Tex" Colbert resigned in 1961 (he did it publicly, like a man, one director said) as Chrysler's market share collapsed to half of its level at the end of Word War II. Into this mess stepped Lynn Townsend, who had come to Chrysler a few years earlier from the auditing firm of Touche Ross. Townsend, now chairman, had been credited with dramatically cutting Chrysler's operating costs and boosting cash flow in the 1950s. John Riccardo, who had worked with Townsend at Touche Ross, became president. Townsend soon dedicated the company's cash flow to a worldwide spending spree, aiming to build Chrysler into a big multinational company like GM and Ford.

Over the following decade Chrysler built plants in Brazil, Argentina, Venezuela, South Africa, and expanded in Australia. But there was no presence in Europe, so Townsend went there looking for acquisitions. He bought Rootes Motors in the United Kingdom, Simca Motors in France, and finally Barriores Diesel in Spain. These were companies on their last legs; UAW President Douglas A. Fraser, who was running the union's Chrysler Division at the time, aptly described them as "dogs." Over two years, my audit teams examined most of these operations. We raced around the world, but these were not joy rides or boondoggles. We made thoughtful and detailed analyses of product engineering, manufacturing operations, scheduling, logistics, quality systems, and productivity. Remember, these were huge operations. Combined, they were larger than Chrysler itself.

The facts we produced were stunning. At Simca, the management was very French in the snootiest sense of the word. There was no way they were going to listen to anyone from the U.S. criticize their quality and productivity. They knew what to do, by God. The only thing they needed from U.S. headquarters was a pile of money to carry out their plans.

At Simca, we started our workday at 7 a.m. Every morning they would send someone to pick us up at the hotel and we'd go to the plant at Nanterre just outside Paris. We'd work until 1 o'clock in the afternoon, and then there was lunch. In the lunchroom, there was always a table covered with bottles of booze, and all the French executives would have a nip or two. I never did. They didn't serve you water with lunch; if you wanted something to drink there was wine, and the Simca executives all helped themselves. These lunches would last until 2:30 or maybe 3:00 in the afternoon. Then we'd go back to work, and pretty soon every executive there would be asleep in his or her office. You couldn't keep them awake! That was their day, from 7 a.m. to 1 p.m., and after lunch and wine, they were completely out of it. The factory workers didn't have it so good; all they got for lunch was beer.

Sometimes the Simca executives would invite us to their homes for a meal. I noticed that in their kitchens they only had tiny refrigerators, so the wives would go shopping every day for the meat, bread, and vegetables for that evening's dinner. Later, when Japanese-style, just-in-time (JIT) parts delivery systems became better known throughout the worldwide auto industry, I would think about the Simca wives. They were practicing a perfect version of JIT in their kitchens, but their husbands didn't have the slightest notion how much an industrial version of that system would tune up their productivity and quality.

At Rootes, the executives didn't drink on the job. It was an old British company that had floundered for years. Its factories were literally run by 21 unions, each independent, and each ready to strike at the drop of a hat. The plant system was as old as it was extensive. Major body panels were stamped in Scotland, and there were assembly operations in Scotland and England. We decided that Chrysler would never have enough cash to modernize there, and it shouldn't even be attempted. Even if Rootes had been capable of efficiency and able to install new technology, the unions would have blocked anything that threatened jobs. Further, we had no management at Highland Park to send overseas to run these operations. Townsend insisted on hiring local executives.

As my audit teams highlighted all the problems, we had to sit through meeting after meeting with the top-level executives at Chrysler who were in charge of implementing Townsend's strategy.

It soon became clear to me that what they really wanted was to soft-peddle these critical audits. But my boss, the corporate general auditor, wasn't cowed. Facts were facts, and he issued our findings without holding back. Later, we found out that only one top executive had taken them to heart: John Riccardo, the president, who recognized the potentially disastrous impact on the company. But it was some time before he could act on his concerns.

After two years on the audit staff, I finally got back into the factory business when they made me manager of manufacturing source and facility planning. After spending so many years in the boondocks and living on the plant floor, the corporate staff environment was completely different to me. All of a sudden I was rubbing shoulders with these starched-shirt guys, and their main job was to please some vice president. The factory workday began at the crack of dawn, but I soon learned that my boss on the staff would be in at 8 o'clock, and at 5 p.m. he was gone. A couple of days a week he might knock off at 1 p.m., and he'd be over at the Oakland Hills Country Club playing golf. You started your day at 7 a.m. or earlier, clearing the deck as best you could, because that vice president was sure to call you in at 9 a.m. with some request or other. Meanwhile, you've got a secretary who's sitting there lining up meeting after meeting for you. It's either a product planning meeting, or a budget meeting, or maybe you're looking at a sourcing decision. This was a complete change of life for me.

My job was to look over the company's vast factory system and make recommendations about the fundamental issues for any business: what do we make, and what do we buy? How do we load assembly plants? What vehicles should be put in them? What kind of flexibility do we have? What engines do we use? What parts do we build? How can we make this the most competitive operation that we can?

Three basic operations were major contributors to cash flow. We assembled cars and trucks; made engines and transmissions; and produced metal stampings for car bodies. But we also had a variety of ancillary plants making parts, seats and interior trim, glass, and the like. The idea was to make them as competitive as possible; but some of them were giving us a hard time. We had four plants making interior trim and seats for cars. One of them, in Ajax, Ontario, was producing premium seats for the Chrysler Imperial® luxury car. One main problem was that the plant couldn't sew straight; the sewing lines on the Imperial seats kept coming out crooked. On top of that, it was taking five or six hours to make a front seat, and we were throwing away tons of expensive material as scrap.

I went up there to find out what was happening. The plant manager said, "Don't worry. I have a big repair crew and we'll take care of this." I went back to the vice president and laid the whole story on his desk. Ajax was unproductive. It wasn't addressing the issue of quality, so I recommended that we send a team there to address quality and productivity or shut the plant down.

Whew! I got reamed from one end to the other. "Don't even discuss productivity," I was told. "This is a quality issue."

"But they go together," I said.

"No, they don't," the vice president said.

The plant remained open. It was years before Chrysler and the rest of the auto industry learned to give production of seats and trim to smart, efficient outside companies like Lear and Johnson Controls.

I spent hours walking every assembly plant. We had to see why we were shipping so many cars with defects. The thing that hit you the minute you walked into an assembly plant was that there were 50 repair stations at the end of every assembly line—that's light repair, where the defect is supposedly easier to identify and fix. And then there were another 10 booths for heavy repair, where workers were practically taking the car apart and rebuilding it. Again, we didn't even try to solve the cause of a problem. You didn't know if it was a vendor problem, design problem, or an assembly issue. Like religion, we'd ship a car with seven or eight defects. We relied on the dealer to fix the defects, although we also knew that in many cases the dealership mechanics wouldn't even be able to figure out why the car wasn't running right.

We were making a lot of money but the question was never asked: How much should we be making? It took us 35 to 40 hours of factory labor to assemble a car. Nobody ever said the target should be 20 hours. Nobody asked: Who is our competition, now and in the future, and how good are they?

Chrysler finally took an equity stake in the Japanese automaker Mitsubishi, and for a few of us, this began to open a window on the world. Mitsubishi wasn't the biggest or the greatest automaker in Japan at the time, but we couldn't get into Toyota and Nissan, who were the big guys. We sent teams over to study Mitsubishi, but even then we didn't try to put together a comprehensive picture of its methods.

The product engineer on the team would come back and tell his people, "They can develop a new car in 32 months, and it takes us 48."

The manufacturing engineer would report to his staff, "They're assembling a car in 20 hours, we're taking 36. They're shipping cars with 2.5 defects per vehicle, and we're running seven or eight. They're making a manual transmission in a couple of hours and we're taking five or six."

What's more, they didn't use armies of quality inspectors like we did. They had control of their processes and worked hard to keep it that way. Nobody stood up to say, how do they do it, and how does product development efficiency affect manufacturing efficiency and quality?

One of our main findings was that the various disciplines involved in car design and production cooperated closely at every point in the process. But we were still walled off from each other. This was partly due to Detroit's longstanding cult of the "car guy." The car guy was an executive who loved automobiles, especially things like style, luxury, power, and speed. It became almost an article of faith in Detroit that a car guy was a better top manager than, say, an expert in finance, who was almost always derided as a "bean counter."

Sometimes people who were fascinated more by finance or the dynamics of manufacturing than by hot cars were reluctant to admit it. Thus, you had top executives coming down to the design studio and ordering changes to cars when they really didn't even know what they were doing. Worse, this attitude meant that designers and product engineers considered themselves the cream of the crop among executives. We manufacturing people were simply the drones who were supposed to shut up and execute the brilliant designs that we were given. There was no corporate focus on manufacturing as a discipline, and no real urgency to get manufacturing people involved in the initial design process. We were forced to make the car or truck against a deadline, even if it couldn't be done with quality or productivity. The designers and product engineers finished up their blueprints and tossed them over the wall to us, and so be it.

One time at Chrysler in the 1970s, a new car design required the use of a wider steel body panel than that of any the manufacturing staff had seen before. This forced a worldwide search to find a steel mill that was making sheet metal that wide. An obsolete mill was finally found that could do it, but certainly not with the productivity, quality, and low cost that we could have had if only the manufacturing engineers had been consulted. This was not just a Chrysler problem. GM, Ford, and American Motors Corp. were in the same boat.

After coming back from one trip to Japan, we made a presentation to all the Chrysler vice presidents about Mitsubishi's advantages, but it went over every man's head. They just didn't want to hear that we weren't the best in quality, productivity, and cost. "The Japanese were just making tiny little cars," they said. "And it doesn't equate to what we're doing here with our complex product line. We are productive. We don't need to follow the Japanese. They don't know what it's like to build big cars. So forget it."

No targets were posted. It was a different world. I also remember an embarrassing moment when a team of Japanese manufacturing experts had been invited to tour our operations in the

U.S. We offered to show them one of our major stamping plants, and they asked to arrive there early enough to watch the daily startup. This plant had 28 major press lines, where body panels went through a series of massive dies that punched the metal into the desired shape. I remember that 24 lines were manned that day. The 7 a.m. starting time arrived. The Japanese executives held their breath in anticipation—and nothing happened. Minutes ticked away, and our visitors noticed that the press operators were just sitting around. "What's happening?" they asked.

"Well," we had to admit, "Everyone is waiting for the union electricians to switch the machines on." Under plant work rules, they were the only ones allowed to do the job, which was not much more complicated than turning on an electric stove. Each electrician had eight press lines to start—but they were all on a coffee break! Scenes like that were the main reason why Japanese automakers later did everything possible to keep the UAW out of their new U.S. plants.

In August of 1975, I was made director of manufacturing engineering planning and services. The rank of director was just below vice president, and now I was one of the corporation's top 70 managers. But I sensed this would be the end of my climb up the executive ladder. I knew I would never make vice president because my mouth was too big; I was too outspoken. And it didn't bother me.

By this time, Chrysler's positive cash flow was quickly disappearing. We must have been losing $20 million a month on overseas operations. The international strategy had been a huge disaster, and it hit home just as the U.S. economy began to fall apart in the late 1970s.

One of the studies we had the manufacturing staff conduct was on whether we should let one of the European companies engineer a small, fuel-efficient car for the American market. They came back and recommended that we build our own design. But upper management vetoed that, saying we should just take a front-wheel drive subcompact that Simca already had in production and buy a 1.8-liter Volkswagen engine and transmission to power it. These were badged as the Dodge Omni and Plymouth Horizon and assembled at Chrysler's assembly plant in northern Illinois. The engine and transmission were fine, but the rest of the car was pretty much a dud. And when the second oil shock hit America in 1979, we were severely limited in the number of these cars we could put on the market. And, we couldn't squeeze Volkswagen to sell us more engines and transmissions.

With a cash crisis at hand in the summer of 1975, Townsend retired and the board of directors named Riccardo as chairman. He immediately set about reversing Townsend's strategy. Everything went on sale. The French automaker Peugeot bought the European division in the early 1980s and South America was sold.

Mitsubishi, which wanted to expand in the Asia-Pacific region, offered to buy our Australian arm after spending weeks studying the operation. The manufacturing complex at Adelaide, Australia was massive. There was a vehicle assembly plant, engine assembly, a metal stamping plant, and even an iron foundry. The plant employed 6,800 people and had seven powerful unions. But it only put out 228 cars per day, which was less than one-third the output of a big assembly plant working at full speed. In other words, the complex spent over 200 man-hours to produce a vehicle.

Mitsubishi's offer, however, came with some interesting strings attached. Chrysler Australia had to reduce quality defects by 90 percent and cut the workforce in half within a year, or there would be no sale. The reaction to this in Highland Park was a huge laugh. There was just no way assembly repairs could be cut by 90 percent and workforce productivity boosted by 40–50 percent in a year! But those goals were largely met. The workforce was reduced to 3,500 making 214 cars per day, a 37 percent productivity gain, and repair work at the end of the assembly line fell enough to meet the objective.

What a lesson! But again, it was lost on upper management. It should have sent a clear signal, particularly to the manufacturing staff, that the era of 3 percent annual productivity improvements was ended. Double-digit gains were not only feasible. If you looked down the road a little and imagined the Japanese coming to America, improvements of that magnitude were a matter of life or death.

Not everything at Chrysler was going wrong. One morning in February, 1977, I got a frantic call from Detroit Edison, our electrical supplier. It was –9° F (–23° C) outside. Coal piles were frozen solid, and the utility was having trouble getting enough coal to keep its Monroe, Michigan generating plant operating at full speed. Edison asked me if Chrysler could cut its electrical use by 10 percent. Fortunately, we had planned for just such an emergency, because the entire Northeast was threatened with energy shortages during that very severe winter. We immediately started calling our plants and telling them to cut non-essential electrical use, and determined that we wouldn't be hurt if we shut the Trenton Engine and Hamtramck car assembly plants for 24 hours. In all, we cut electricity use by more than 13 percent, and the crisis was over. Somehow the story got out. I was featured Feb. 23, 1977 in a front-page story in the *Wall Street Journal* that portrayed Chrysler as a model for the nation in energy planning. It was flattering to see my name in print; I had no idea that it would shortly become a common, and sometimes painful, sight.

But our larger problems continued to drag us down. About this time, Chrysler was retooling its Lynch Road assembly plant in Detroit to build a new full-sized car. One day the vice president in charge of assembly plants called some 200 people together for a presentation on the vehicle. "It will have the highest quality in the industry," he said. "The company will put 640 inspectors in the plant to insure quality." That was 5,120 added labor hours per day, or eight additional hours per car.

I remember standing up and saying, "We can't afford this, and it will not result in a quality car. We can't afford to put this car on the street if you're adding all those labor hours."

"We must do this; we must ensure quality," he said.

By then we had seen how Mitsubishi relied on production workers to do a good job, making sure that the individual assembly line job was set up so it was easier to do right than wrong. But upper management in Detroit still had that mindset: You had one worker to do a job, and another to check whether the job was done right.

The new full-sized car turned into a quality disaster and didn't last very long on the market. Neither did the plant where it was built. Lynch Road assembly was among those closed permanently when the ax began to fall on Chrysler's domestic operations in the 1980–81 economic crisis. Other casualties included a car assembly plant in the Detroit enclave of Hamtramck; the Missouri Truck assembly plant; a smaller assembly plant in Warren, Michigan that built large Class-A motor home chassis; stamping plants at Eight Mile Road and Outer Drive, and at Mack Avenue in Detroit; an engine assembly plant in Windsor, Ontario; foundries on Huber Avenue in Detroit and in Fostoria, Ohio; and several other smaller plants that made interior trim. We had been lax and we were paying the price.

By late 1979, the atmosphere at Chrysler headquarters was getting grim, especially on the 5th floor of the K.T. Keller building where top executives had their offices. At 4 o'clock one evening, a group of four of us was riding the escalator up to the 5th floor when we saw a young woman, whom we knew was on the legal staff, on her way down. She was carrying a big legal folder and on the side of it we could see the word, BANKRUPTCY.

"Oh my God, nobody told us!" I said. Startled, we ran up to confront our boss.

"Is this true?" we asked. It turned out that he didn't know anything about it either. We later found out that she was a law student at Wayne State University and one of her classes that term was in bankruptcy law. We could relax—but not for long.

In September, 1978, Riccardo rocked Detroit by hiring Lee A. Iacocca as Chrysler president. Iacocca had recently been fired as president of Ford Motor Co. by Chairman Henry Ford II. "Hank the Deuce," as Detroiters knew him, later explained that he didn't think Iacocca was qualified to succeed him as the No. 2 automaker's top executive. "Among other things," Ford said,

"Iacocca lacked international experience." But the word at the time was that Ford had told Iacocca, "I just don't like you." Lee had gotten too big for his britches at Ford, forgetting his place; he was hired help, while the Ford family members were royalty. Iacocca deeply resented this humiliation, and we were soon to find out exactly how much.

One day Iacocca came to the styling center at Highland Park to see the new minivan that we had in the works. It was a new concept by Hal Sperlich, a talented car guy who had been tossed out of Ford earlier after quarreling with Henry Ford II over future product plans. Vans had been somewhat popular before this; in fact, Chrysler did a nice business with some of its big van products. But these were based on pickup truck chassis; they were big, guzzled gas, and rode like the trucks that they were. The minivan combined the features of a car and truck. It was small enough to fit in your garage and had a relatively fuel-efficient, front-drive powertrain, but it had plenty of space for a family and luggage.

I watched as Iacocca went over the vehicle. He suggested a few changes, and then we heard him mutter: "Now I've got them right by the ass." We all sat there wondering what he meant, but no one asked. A month or so later the changes had been made and he came back for another look. "I really have them now. This is exactly what I want," he said.

We finally asked him what in the heck he was talking about. "Well, who makes the most station wagons in the world?" he said.

"Ford does," we answered.

"That's what I mean," Iacocca said. "This will tear them apart."

Unfortunately, Chrysler didn't have the money at the time to put the minivan into production. But the resources arrived later from an unusual source. In July of 1979, Chrysler reported that it lost $200 million in the second quarter and needed financial aid. Since the government had helped Chrysler get into this situation by imposing all those regulations, the government should help with a bailout. Riccardo's first request was for a $1.5 billion tax break. But soon Riccardo was gone, and Iacocca took over as chairman. The government offered to consider a bailout in the form of guaranteed loans. In effect, the feds would co-sign a $1.5 billion note. But first, Chrysler had to go through the gut-wrenching process of slimming down and getting concessions from workers, suppliers, bankers, and just about everyone connected with it. In reality it was no different from a bankruptcy proceeding, except that it was handled out of court. "Nobody would buy cars from a bankrupt company," Iacocca said.

I was assigned to represent manufacturing on the task force that was working on the bailout with the federal government. There were about 80 of us, including Chrysler workers, the government people, bankers, and others, all under the supervision of Steve Miller, the former Ford executive who later became a corporate turnaround artist. Ultimately we got it all together, and the bailout was ready for final approval.

Then one day we had a visit from Treasury Secretary Bill Miller, whose department was supervising the bailout. Miller had just gotten off a Northwest Airlines commercial flight from Washington when he discovered that Iacocca had flown on one of Chrysler's corporate jets to visit the New York Yankees spring training camp in Florida. Newspapers had shown pictures of Iacocca relaxing in the Yankees' dugout with team owner George Steinbrenner. This had to end, Miller decided. He told Steve Miller and me that we had one more thing to do: Chrysler had to get rid of its corporate jets; taxpayers wouldn't like the idea that they were backing a plan to have executives fly around the country in style and comfort. We were to go and break the news to Iacocca.

You could have scraped Iacocca off the ceiling. For years he had been accustomed to traveling around the world in private airplanes well stocked with booze and his favorite cigars, and now he was supposed to travel commercial? Oh, my! But he found a way out of that humiliation. The jets were sold to a Swiss leasing company and then immediately leased back to Chrysler, where they kept flying. Years later, when a slimmed-down Chrysler was making a lot of money from the mid-1980s car sales boom, Lee got even by buying Gulfstream Aerospace, the manufacturer of luxury corporate jets.

The story of the bailout has been told in great detail elsewhere, and I don't need to repeat it. Chrysler ended up taking $1.2 billion in loan guarantees. That gave Lee the money to put minivans on the market along with the new K-car, which was later elaborated into a whole host of styles and versions. The loans were paid back ahead of schedule, and the government even made money on the deal by exercising warrants to buy Chrysler stock that it had demanded as part of the deal.

But I never got the chance to share in the fun days of Chrysler's recovery. For the second time in my career, the ax struck me personally. On April 1, 1980, after 23 years with the company, I was back on the street.

Chapter 4
My Turn to Go

"A businessman is a servant, and when he gets too rich, or too high and mighty for that, then something happens, and someone else gets a chance. And this is occurring on a large scale now. Thus it comes, reasonably enough, that a period of bad business is really a good thing for business, because it drives business back to its sounder fundamentals of honor in negotiations, quality in merchandise, and willingness in service."
—Henry Ford, in "Today and Tomorrow," 1930

My boss, a vice president of manufacturing, called me into his office that morning at 9 a.m. When I got to the outer office, his secretary quickly shut the door behind me. She was an attractive lady, whom I had known for years, but today her head was down and she didn't want our eyes to meet. I sensed what was about to happen, and frankly I wasn't surprised. For the past four months I had worked exclusively as the top manufacturing executive on the bailout task force, and that job had essentially been completed the preceding Friday. I came to this meeting knowing it would be about my fate—whether I was to be promoted, demoted, reassigned or fired. I recall that the inner office was darkened with the blinds drawn. My boss's desk was surprisingly clean, with just one piece of paper in view. He gave me the word quickly: the corporate manufacturing engineering staff that I had led was being eliminated. I would be reassigned to another job with less responsibility—a demotion.

I wasn't the first old Chrysler hand to hear this. After John Riccardo had retired as chairman and given the top job to Iacocca, several top Chrysler execs had been booted out, many of them replaced by former Iacocca cronies from Ford Motor Co. But I knew that some of them had been offered early retirement, so I spoke up. "Since you're eliminating my department and my job, you have to give me the option to retire," I said. My boss evidently hadn't expected to hear this. He told me he needed time to look into my request and excused me.

Returning to my office, I thought about my wife. She had endured a lot, especially in those early days when our family was growing and I was working full time and going to school. Everybody in Detroit knew about Chrysler's problems, but I hadn't told her that my job might be in jeopardy. I was 52; we had a 12-year-old daughter at home and two kids in college.

I was called back to my boss's office at 1 p.m. This time the secretary and I exchanged greetings, and I knew there was cause for hope. I found there was good news and bad. His boss, an executive vice president, had approved my request for retirement. I breathed: whew! "*But*," he said, "that would be at age 55." I would have to leave immediately. There would be no severance pay, and my health insurance would be canceled until I reached retirement age. I would have to turn in my assigned car, as well as the one that I had leased on favorable terms as another executive perk. This was sobering, to say the least.

I drove home, one-half hour away up Interstate 75, wondering how to tell my wife that I now had no paycheck and no car, and that I would have no pension or hospitalization for three years. When I got home I said, "Dear, I think we ought to go out on the back porch and have a drink." She reminded me that we never drank during the week. "Today we do," I said. "I don't have a job anymore."

The next day I went back to Highland Park to pack up my personal belongings. Unexpectedly, I got a telephone call that changed my life.

Here's some background: By the mid-1970s, the U.S. Department of Transportation (DOT) was getting directly involved in the auto industry. This was understandable on a couple of levels. First, the private automobile was America's primary mode of transportation, like it or not. Unlike Europe and Japan, mass transit in America was a road to nowhere—largely still is. Secondly, American auto executives had resisted the government's drive to impose new safety, clean air, and fuel economy regulations. For the most part, executives from Detroit had told the feds that the regulations couldn't be met; or, if they could be met, nobody would want to buy the cars that resulted. The feds didn't believe it, and U.S. automakers lost all credibility at the Capitol. Some of the cars that today are collectors' gold were being described as "insolent chariots." And hadn't George Romney, the president of American Motors Corp., castigated the Big Three for building "gas-guzzling dinosaurs?"

The DOT then began a major effort to get an objective and accurate picture of the industry through internal studies of its own, focusing especially on Detroit's ability to make small, fuel-efficient cars and trucks. A regional office in Boston had been assigned to lead the study, partly under the direction of Dick John. He had a group of analysts who were becoming automotive experts like George Byron, John O'Donald, and Marty Anderson. They worked to build a strategic base of data on how the industry was structured, how it functioned, and how long it took to produce a new or substantially redesigned vehicle. Similar comparative studies of the European and Japanese auto industries were also attempted. Chrysler accommodated members of this group, showing them its main assembly and manufacturing plants. I'm told that GM and Ford did the same. Part of my job, at the time, was to educate this crew, so I got to know them pretty well.

On my last day at Chrysler, Dr. John (as we invariably called him) telephoned to ask if I could fly to Boston for a high-level meeting with some DOT personnel from Washington.

"Sorry, I'm just packing up my personal belongings," I replied. "I no longer work at Chrysler."

"Come up anyway," he said. "You can help me, and I believe I can help you."

"Who's paying for this trip?" I asked.

"You are," he said.

I couldn't think of a good reason to refuse, so in a few days I found myself sitting in his office in Cambridge with a senior partner of the Arthur D. Little management consulting firm. This individual told me that Arthur D. Little was looking for an auto executive to help them in a large study ("large" at that time meaning a $5–$6 million fee) being done for "a major Japanese automaker." The job would last about six months, and I would get a consulting fee of $600 per day. That was a huge daily rate, and I had a hard time believing it. But I signed on; I had been unemployed less than a week.

They didn't tell me who had commissioned the study until we were ready to leave for Japan and I had signed a ream of confidentiality agreements: Toyota. The company was considering building an assembly plant in the United States. Its domestic competitors, Honda and Nissan, were already on their way there. Toyota wanted a large site. It had to accommodate an assembly plant to build 1,000 cars per day and an attached metal stamping facility. The site also had to be large enough so that capacity for assembly and stamping could be doubled when Toyota's U.S. market share was big enough.

Toyota was extremely leery of the UAW. It would consider a site in the Midwest because so many skilled hourly and salaried automotive workers lived there. But the company wasn't afraid of taking on the task of training an entire workforce if that turned out to be the safest solution.

Toyota leaders also wanted to know: what products should they make in the U.S.? Should they just assemble cars and import engines and transmissions from Japan, or should they build engine and transmission manufacturing plants in America? What were parts suppliers like? Could they handle Toyota's strict requirements for quality, low cost, and sharp delivery performance?

The team, which included four people from Arthur D. Little and me, spent the next three months in Japan, on and off. Understand, I had been to Mitsubishi, but Toyota literally stunned me—this was a new world. They took us to every plant—assembly, engine, transmission, you name it. We walked every foot of these operations, including some of the company's suppliers. I went to one of its foundries making cast iron blocks for Toyota's four-cylinder engines. Next door was a forging plant making crankshafts and connecting rods. These were physically the cleanest plants I had ever seen in my life. It wasn't a foundry as I had known them; it wasn't a forge plant as I had known them, with crap all over the floor. Toyota management showed us literally everything. One day they said, here's our expert on just-in-time production, and he spent a whole day with us. Here's our expert on assembly plant quality; here's how we do quality at machining plants. We spent a day listening to quality circles, the groups of workers on the plant floor who met every day to discuss quality issues.

The product engineering session just blew me away. I was with an engineer who worked exclusively on body firewalls, the panel between the engine and passenger compartments. He pulled them all up on a computer—a pretty crude system in those days compared to today—and every damned one looked alike. On different models, the holes in the firewall for steering, wiring, heating, and the like were all in the same place. The same with door panels and instrument panels—they were common, common, common. By making them and mounting them the same way on different vehicles, Toyota saved a ton of money. Needless to say, at Chrysler a different model had a different firewall, door panel, or instrument panel mounting system from the next model, meaning you had to have a different set of tools to make them.

In every plant we were handed a ton of data; manpower by department, the quality systems in use, and detailed listings of problems by operation. We were buried in the kind of detail that I had never seen before. Every night at dinner we would throw questions at Toyota executives, and they seemed perfectly prepared. We never heard a single one say, "I don't know the answer to that, but I'll try to find out." At that time, General Motors had begun to experiment with the use of robots in car production. But robots were not in widespread use in the U.S., and here not at all. Toyota's efficiency wasn't a matter of technology, but of system. Every day I saw examples of things that I had thought were impossible:

- There was a total absence of cardboard on the assembly lines. In U.S. plants, many parts arrived in cardboard containers, and the stuff was everywhere, creating massive disposal problems. We had to buy huge shredders to get rid of it.

- All major components were delivered to the assembly line in small lot sizes. In some U.S. plants, the component inventories were often stacked to the roof and, in some spots, these piles of inventory almost blocked your view of the production line.

- Assemblers didn't have to sort out which components went with which vehicle; when bumper fascias, instrument panels, seats, and other systems arrived at the assembly line, they were sequenced for the vehicle moving down the line at that moment.

- Metal body panels were made on a major press for just two days of production. In North America, the production lot size for metal stampings was a minimum of 10 days and, in most cases, 20 days. Compared to Toyota, I saw that we had been wasting money on large inventories of steel body panels that were prone to damage when they were put in and out of storage.

- It took Toyota workers 5–6 minutes to change dies in a stamping press to switch production from one body panel to another. That compared with 4–6 hours (and sometimes up to 24 hours) in Big-Three plants. In the 1960s and 1970s, when Detroit had large production runs of a single vehicle line—a full-sized Chevrolet would sell two million copies a year—it made some sense to fill your warehouse with a single part before changing the press over to make another one. If that massive run of Chevy Impala® hoods turned out to be defective, however, you were saddled with tremendous waste. In addition, metal stampings are fragile and damage prone. The more you handle them, in and out of storage, the more likely they'll be bent or scratched. By 1980, the market was changing; the vehicle lineup was becoming more complex, and the need to produce numerous models at lower volume meant that slow die changes would kill you. Here was Toyota putting out a car with about one-third the investment in stamping presses that Detroit needed, and without huge inventories that gobbled investment and produced immense amounts of scrap.

- Stamping presses that were engineered to run 10 to 15 strokes per minute or 600 to 900 pieces per hour ran 10 to 15 strokes per minute. On a good day at Chrysler, we ran 7 or 8 strokes per minute. Again, I could hardly believe it; Toyota was getting twice the output of body panels per minute, per hour, per day.

- Stamping press downtime was carefully measured and whatever caused the problem was immediately corrected. Again, workers didn't just take a bad part out of the press and start up again; they worked to find and fix the cause of the problem. Actual downtime was less than 5 percent of scheduled production time on an 8-hour shift, compared with press lines in the U.S. that averaged 8 hours of production over two 8-hour shifts.

- Stamped panels had no sharp edges because the dies were constantly maintained. A few stamped panels from the final hour of production every day were put aside for a detailed quality inspection. If the panel was not within specification, the plant had 48 hours to bring the offending die up to its quality specification. U.S.-built cars at this time often had ill-fitting body panels, with gaps between, say, a door and fender that varied considerably from side-to-side and car-to-car. At Toyota, the body panel fit was usually perfect.

- Painting car bodies is a difficult, delicate operation. This is true even today when it is generally done with paint robots. In those days, most painting was by hand; masked and coated workers stood in a booth and sprayed the bodies with paint guns as they went past. Dirt and dust were always a problem, not to mention over-spraying, under-spraying, or the occasional orange-peel problem. At Chrysler, 30 percent of paint jobs were defective on the first try and had to be repaired; the company used separate high-bake ovens just to handle repainting off the main conveyor line at a cost of millions of dollars. At Toyota, 95 percent of car bodies went through the paint shop without needing repair. There were no separate high-bake repair ovens. The main difference was that Chrysler had a system that would tolerate repairs and Toyota didn't; each Toyota worker was responsible for making sure that the body was painted correctly. This was one of the major keys to what later became famously known as the Toyota Production System (TPS).

- Toyota assembly plants had only five repair booths at the end of the assembly line, and often we noted that there weren't any cars in them undergoing fine-tuning or deeper rework. Almost all U.S. assembly plants had 40–50 stations at the end of the line for minor repairs and another 10 for heavy repairs. They were always full.

- Toyota assembly plants measured about 1.8 million ft^2 (167,220 m^2) for output of 1,000 cars per day. In the 1970s and 1980s, General Motors was in the process of building new assembly plants around the U.S.—at 3.2 million ft^2 (297,280 m^2) for the same 1,000 cars per day. Much of that space at GM was designed to handle large parts inventories. Toyota didn't have large parts inventories. You can just imagine the difference in overhead costs.

- Every Toyota plant seemed immaculately clean. What was more startling, each production worker cleaned his own station. North American plants employed armies of janitors. Under UAW work rules, production line workers weren't required or even allowed to clean up their workstations.

- Toyota workers had a union too. The Japanese auto industry had seen some serious labor disputes and strikes in the 1950s, but a permanent peace had been made between management and unions. At Toyota, all union officers were also full-time production workers. U.S. plants employed 30–40 union officers and representatives who didn't work on the line. Their job was to write grievances.

- You often saw manufacturing and product engineers working together on the plant floor to get at the root cause of production problems. In the U.S., it was almost impossible to get product engineers to visit a factory—it was beneath their dignity.

- Absenteeism at Toyota hardly existed. In contrast, it was normal in U.S. plants to average 8–10 percent unexcused absences on Mondays and, on Fridays, there seemed to be no limit. In effect, every plant manager and shop foreman showed up at work every day wondering how he was going to fill all the jobs on the line. Now that's great for quality; rounding up workers for jobs for which they hadn't been trained. Assembly-line jobs are difficult, and experienced workers will develop a comfortable rhythm. An average U.S. assembly plant making 1,000 cars per day would employ about 4,500 workers. But 350–450 of them on average would be absent every day, causing major workmanship headaches. And the UAW would fight every attempt to put disciplinary programs in place.

- Most employees were members of quality circles. Toyota management used these groups as a sort of icing on the quality cake. They would fine-tune a system that had been honed to efficiency at every production step leading up to final assembly.

In short, the Arthur D. Little team was the first American group to get a complete tutorial on the Toyota Production System, in which quality control extended from the end of the assembly line back through manufacturing engineering and product engineering. Toyota was not just a company; it was a family that included major parts manufacturers like truck manufacturer Hino and the giant Nippondenso electrical concern (now known as Denso); and those children were mirror images of the parent when it came to quality and productivity.

In retrospect, the Toyota Production System that we studied in 1980 was still in its infancy, especially compared to the global behemoth that Toyota has become. When we got back home, the team struggled to absorb everything we had seen. What was the secret? Was it Toyota's focus on product engineering, manufacturing engineering, design for quality, the reliance on common assembly-line workstations to build in quality, just-in-time parts management systems, quality circles, or extensive commonality in all designs and manufacturing processes? Or, was it the way they all linked together? Would this system work in the U.S.?

As we were writing our report, I beat my brains out trying to quantify the major areas that contributed to Toyota's success. I knew that we had a big story on our hands. The bottom line seemed to be that U.S. automakers just couldn't compete with the Japanese; they were so far behind that it would take ages to catch up. When it was time to break this news to Detroit, people there would want proof, and I wanted to be prepared to back it up with facts.

We've seen how this played out. Toyota, ever cautious and conservative, got into U.S. manufacturing with a half-step trial. In 1984, it formed a joint venture with General Motors named New United Motor Manufacturing Inc., commonly known as NUMMI. It involved a single U.S. plant at Fremont, California, which had been one of GM's trouble spots. This was the first test of the Toyota Production System in the U.S. Then, in 1986, it went the whole hog, establishing the gigantic assembly and manufacturing complex at Georgetown, Kentucky.

Today, the Toyota system is legendary. Just about everyone, at least in the auto industry, has heard about Taiichi Ohno. He was the machine shop operator who came to the U.S. in 1956 to visit American auto plants, but was most impressed by the way supermarkets kept their shelves stocked. Ohno, who became a Toyota executive vice president, used that epiphany to establish the TPS and the so-called five-why process—if there's a problem in production and you ask yourself "why" five times, you'll get to the root cause. Today, manufacturing engineers and industrial historians in the U.S. are taught "Ohnoism" along with "Fordism." But in the latter part of 1980, I was one of just a handful of people in America who knew anything about it.

Chapter 5

The Atom Bomb

"Harbour put all the pieces together and exposed the
productivity issue outside the auto industry
in a way that had never been done before."
—*William J. Harahan, director of manufacturing planning,*
Ford Motor Co., February 27, 1982

"We have looked at the 'Harbour Report'
and believe he doesn't have the right documentation
to verify his conclusions, especially in productivity."
—*Lydia Fisher, UAW economist, February, 1982*

Back in the U.S., I focused initially on helping the Arthur D. Little team write up their study for Toyota. But I knew I had the ammunition to write the first *Harbour Report*, and I thought it was explosive. I was sitting there on pins and needles. One, I didn't know how to tell the story. Two, I didn't know who to tell it to. Should I go to the auto companies, or to the newspapers? I didn't know any reporters. Anyway, I was a nobody, and who would listen to me?

The day after I left Chrysler I had decided to form Harbour & Associates as a manufacturing consulting company. As far as I knew, nothing like it really existed; but I sensed that manufacturing improvement would be the auto industry's big drive in the 1980s, and that automakers and suppliers would need help. That's pretty much how it played out. But now, after finishing up at Arthur D. Little, I wasn't working for anyone.

I had tons of data about the Toyota Production System, and I knew Chrysler's by heart. I had visited GM and Ford plants, and I knew that their problems were similar to those at Chrysler. But

I spent a considerable amount of time collecting data on Ford and GM manufacturing systems. Those two companies weren't particularly helpful, but a great deal of data was publicly available on their product output and staffing levels. There was no public information on quality.

Dave Power was just beginning the annual surveys of defect rates in new cars and trucks that would later become famous as the *J. D. Power Report*. Sifting all this data, my goal was to estimate the production cost difference between Toyota and the Detroit firms. Slowly it came into focus: Toyota was able to put a small car for sale in the U.S. at a manufactured cost $1,500 below similar products from GM, Ford, and Chrysler. At the time, the factory sales price of cars in this segment—in other words, the amount that dealers paid for the car before they took their markup—was about $4,600. In this calculation, Toyota's cost advantage was about 33 percent! The number was startling, but it seemed to fit with the differences in manufacturing efficiency that I had seen at Toyota. The implication was that Toyota could run amok in the U.S. market. It was getting one-third more revenue per small car than the domestic manufacturers at the same retail price. That meant it could put more features and gadgets in its cars; add whatever hardware was needed to make better seats, and smoother and quieter engines; and still have enough left over for whiz-bang advertising campaigns. And even with all those product and marketing advantages, it would still be making a tidy profit.

On a final visit to Arthur D. Little in Boston, I went to see Dr. Richard John, director of the Volpe Center at the U.S. Department of Transportation's (DOT's) auto industry study office in Cambridge, Massachusetts. "Doc," I said, "here's the story," and I showed him my basic research. He was excited; this was exactly the kind of comparative data that DOT had been angling for all along. He wanted to show the results to Transportation Secretary Neil Goldschmidt and other higher-ups at DOT. But he thought it would be better first to show my data to the Detroit auto companies and listen to their reactions.

So we started a parade of meetings, beginning at Ford on September 23, 1980, with a follow-up on October 24. I found that people at Ford had been doing their homework. The No. 2 automaker was affiliated with Japanese automaker Mazda, and had visited Mazda at Hiroshima in a series of comparative productivity studies. Ford's manufacturing experts told me that my data didn't conflict with theirs; they thought I was well within the ballpark. My getting that much confirmation was a huge relief.

The next meeting, I knew, would be a major test. Dr. John and George Byron of DOT in Boston had set up a meeting with General Motors officials in the boardroom at the company's office tower in New York. We were asked to be there an hour before the meeting to have lunch with David Collier, a GM vice president. He wanted a summary of what I would say; he didn't want to waste his valuable time at the meeting if it wasn't going to be anything notable. "General Motors plants are unproductive, low-quality operations," I told him. "You know, the Japanese are sitting there assembling a car at Toyota in 15 hours."

Then he told me he wasn't going to the meeting because GM's plan at the new plants it was then building was to get down to 15 hours direct labor as well. "Gee, that's fine, but you're not listening," I said. "That 15 hours at Toyota includes direct labor, the workers who are actually putting the car together as it passes down the line. And it also includes all salaried workers as well as indirect hourly labor such as janitors, forklift operators, and maintenance workers." I didn't know what a comparable figure would be at GM, but it was certainly a lot more than 15 hours per car. And that was just the tip of the iceberg. Collier picked up the phone and told his secretary he would be at the meeting as long as it lasted.

I couldn't believe my eyes when I walked into the boardroom with the two DOT employees. There were at least 40 seats around the big table and they were all filled. Another 40 or so seats around the room were occupied by second-tier executives and staffers. I had been in similar meetings at Chrysler, but there it was a smaller group. I got a strong sense of how big and powerful

GM was as they directed me to sit in GM Chairman Tom Murphy's seat at the center of the table. The crowd included executives from assembly operations, stamping, engine and transmission manufacturing, an assistant controller, and the company's treasury department staff. All the big guns were there, and soon I found that I was their target. My presentation lasted 45 minutes, and for the next two hours these executives challenged both my data and my interpretation of it. Things got to be pretty confrontational.

Their main issue was GM's so-called southern strategy. The company didn't call it that, but everyone else did. GM was building massive new 3.2-million-ft^2 (297,280-m^2) assembly plants in North America, many of them in anti-union southern states. They told me that these plants would be super-efficient, and they wouldn't have to deal with the UAW since many would be in right-to-work states. "When this renovation is complete," they said, "GM will be the most efficient auto company in the world as well as the biggest. As for Toyota, it just builds small cars, which is a simple matter compared with the GM lineup of small, medium, large, and luxury cars and trucks."

I decided to take them on—my way. "Toyota only needs 1.8 million ft^2 (167,220 m^2) of factory space to assemble 1,000 cars a day, compared with your 3.2 million," I told them. They didn't buy it. We got into discussions of metal stamping, engine and transmission manufacturing—everything I had seen at Toyota. In effect, they told me I was full of it.

On November 25, we made our presentation at Chrysler. Of course, I knew every face in the crowd. When I was finished, the Chrysler executives just got up and left without a lot of discussion. They obviously did not want to hear this kind of message from one of their deposed executives.

We even made a presentation to the UAW brass at Solidarity House, their Detroit headquarters. They also disputed my analysis. Later, when the bomb had dropped publicly, the UAW put out a statement saying that I had not done my homework and that my conclusion was not supported by facts.

Soon, however, I had some favorable input from GM. On December 8, 1980, I was invited to a meeting at GM's sprawling technical center in Warren, Michigan. There I met Alex Mair, who was the group vice president in charge of technical staffs, as well as the assistant controller who had attended the meeting in New York. These officials knew that GM had a problem. They wanted to analyze the company's viability and develop a comprehensive plan to make the No. 1 automaker more competitive. This time the discussion was very positive. Mair was a smart, creative guy with whom I developed a longstanding friendship. He soon became the inspiration for GM's Saturn® project, an all-out effort by GM to field a U.S.-built small car that was competitive in cost and quality with the Japanese. In later years he'd frequently call me up and ask for my opinion on what GM was doing to boost quality and productivity. But the company's top officials were still in deep denial.

Later that month I was called to another meeting at GM, where I was asked to wait a year before delivering my report publicly so that the company would have more time to study the issue and draw up an improvement plan. I didn't know it then, but GM soon would be sending armies over to Japan to see if I had been right. Anyway, it was too late to hold the report.

On December 12 we met in Washington with Transportation Secretary Goldschmidt and his staff. They were deeply impressed, and wanted to release the report publicly as a DOT study. "Be my guest," I said. Goldschmidt even put his name on it, which was okay with me. I had also been working over the past several months with William Abernathy, a Harvard business professor. He helped me put the report into a more polished form. Bill was easy to work with, and his analytical skills were superb. He took a lot of credit for it, and that was fine—I didn't have any problem with that. We became good friends, but unfortunately he had terminal cancer and would die shortly after the report became public. The secretary of transportation was required to issue a report to the President annually on the state of the automotive industry. So on Jan. 11, 1981, he submitted his report entitled "The U.S. Automobile Industry, 1980."

I had been at Bikini Atoll when the U.S. exploded two atomic bombs, and that was spectacular (see Figure 5-1). But now the Goldschmidt pronouncement that it costs the Big-Three automakers $1,500 more than Toyota to put a small car on the market seemed like an even bigger blast. I was totally on the sidelines at first; DOT didn't identify me for a month. Everybody was going after Abernathy, especially the news media. He finally started telling people, "Look, I only did part of this. Harbour is the guy who did it all, so give him a call." Soon my phone was ringing constantly. I was spending hours answering questions from the press and from the automakers. You couldn't satisfy the reporters' appetites. I think for six weeks I spent all day, every day, talking to reporters. Then came requests for speeches or other presentations, and some of these were grueling. I remember giving a detailed presentation to a group of professors at Stanford University. After my talk, these people spent a great deal of time and effort tearing me apart. But none of that bothered me.

Reaction from the U.S. automakers was pretty much as I expected. Ford was first to respond. They told reporters that my findings were almost identical to the studies that they conducted

Figure 5-1. Atomic bomb blast at Bikini Atoll, 1946.

at Mazda. Chrysler said they hadn't seen the research and couldn't comment on it. GM was still in absolute, profound denial—at least in public. I was now talking regularly with some GM executives about my findings, and they were very interested in getting to the bottom of it.

I had used some of my Mitsubishi data in the analysis, but Toyota was the primary focus. Toyota leaders had given me permission to publicly discuss what I had seen in their plants, but they wanted me to agree not to expose any of their sensitive technology. I had no problem with that, since in all the visits I had made to their plants, I never saw any interesting new technology. There were no new machines, no radical new processes, nothing different to the eye from what you would see in a U.S. plant. Toyota never was, and still is not, a big fan of new technology for its own sake. Tight management control of all of its manufacturing processes was, and remains, the company's secret technology. After the report came out, Toyota leaders gave me some more input, saying I had overstated some things and understated others. But the funny thing was, they were glad that the report was out. It was only later that they became irked because so many people wanted to send squadrons of people to Nagoya to study Toyota operations.

GM remained a hard sell for some time. An incident that happened somewhat later hints at the problem. In August of 1982, my name had been bandied about so much that I was invited to speak at the Automotive News World Congress, a major annual conference where auto topics are discussed by some of the industry's top people. (*Automotive News* is a weekly trade newspaper covering the industry.) I was to be the first speaker in a Monday morning session.

Meanwhile F. James McDonald, president of GM, had been tabbed to deliver the keynote speech on Sunday night. The topic of his speech was "Gaining the Competitive Edge." On Sunday evening before the speech, my wife, Dolores, and I had the privilege of having dinner at a downtown Detroit hotel with Jim McDonald and his wife. We had a brief conversation about the industry's future direction, but we didn't talk about the speeches we were going to deliver. After dinner, McDonald gave his presentation, and at the end of it he said, "I have one last comment to make. When I die, I want to come back in my second life as an automotive consultant. Then I could show these consultants who are around today how to really analyze an auto company."

I was livid. Seething, I went down to my hotel room and rewrote the end of my speech. I was speaking on quality and productivity and our Japanese competition. At the end of my talk I said, "I thought Mr. McDonald gave a great speech last night and I noticed that, in his second life, he wants to come back as an automotive consultant and teach us how to do our job. When I die I also want to come back. In my second life, I want to be the president of General Motors." GM's public relations vice president was sitting right in front of me in the audience, and I could see him turn red. Later, I was told on many occasions that a letter had gone out from McDonald's office communicating that Jim Harbour was never to be allowed on any GM property.

It was a few years before I was officially back in GM's good graces, but I have no regrets. My speech that morning was positive, direct, and without any sugar coating. That's always been my way.

Chapter 6

At Warner-Lambert

"If you think of standardization as the best that you know today, but which is to be improved tomorrow—you get somewhere."

"Business is never so healthy as when, like a chicken, it must do a certain amount of scratching for what it gets."
—Henry Ford

"Thank you for the thought-provoking presentation. Best of luck and continued success in spreading the gospel on quality and productivity."
—Hans-Ulrich Bodenmann, president, Capsugel, in a letter to James E. Harbour

I was becoming famous, or maybe notorious, but it wasn't help-ing me earn a living. That first year I got a small contract from the U.S. Department of Transportation, and I kept updating the Toyota study. Harbour & Associates sold a few of those, and that helped keep us afloat. But the first year in business was a financial loss. Actually, it was a financial disaster. But I wasn't interested in making a lot of money. Nobody else was offering the same kind of service; at least, nobody with the same kind of deep manufacturing background. I had a couple of Chrysler retirees working with me, and we weren't doing a whole lot of outside consulting.

Then on a Sunday afternoon in March, 1982, well into our second year, I got a call from the plant manager of Capsugel, a division of the pharmaceutical and consumer products giant War-ner-Lambert. He said the president of Capsugel, a Swiss fellow named Hans-Ulrich Bodenmann, had read a story about quality in the *New York Times* while on a transatlantic flight. The story had highlighted the major differences between the Japanese and

North American automakers. It said the Japanese could build a car for $1,700 less than the U.S. domestic manufacturers. A major focus of the article was quality, and it noted that the Japanese quality system was based on defect prevention while the U.S. producers relied on inspection and repair. The story hit Bodenmann like a bomb. Capsugel made empty gelatin capsules for the pharmaceutical industry. When he read the *New York Times* story, he was on his way to visit Pfizer Corp., one of his biggest customers, and they were just going to kill him. They were going to eat him alive because the quality of the gelatin capsules was so poor. So, the plant manager asked if I could be in Greenwood, South Carolina the next morning to take a look at the capsule manufacturing operations there. "Forget it," I said. "I can't be there tomorrow morning. How about Wednesday?"

I did fly down a couple of days later. I wasn't exactly swamped with auto industry work, and I thought it would be fascinating to see if what I had learned in automotive plants could be applied in other industries. It was the beginning of a productive, mutually beneficial 20-year relationship with Warner-Lambert and others in the pharmaceutical industry.

Capsugel had plants in Europe and Japan as well as in South Carolina. Bodenmann's office was in Basel, Switzerland, which by the way, is a delightful place to visit. He had been told that the only way to fix quality problems at the Greenwood plant was to scrap the 40 capsule machines designed in 1916 that they were using and design and install all new ones. But that would cost $150 million, and Bodenmann wasn't about to sign a check for that, nor was Warner-Lambert. The mandate was to fix the problem or get out of that business. I didn't know that. I didn't even know how to spell "pharmaceuticals." My first thought was that, since the pharmaceutical industry was regulated heavily by the U.S. Food & Drug Administration, it must have pretty high quality.

So I flew to Greenville and rented a car for the 50-mile drive to the Greenwood plant. Preoccupied, I didn't notice how fast I was driving. But a nice South Carolina police officer did, and wrote me out a $50 speeding ticket.

The next morning I met with a group of Capsugel executives, including the head of worldwide manufacturing, and we started a round of plant visits. The place was immaculately clean, just what you would expect when you're making something that people put in their mouths. I had to wear a gown, and hat and shoe covers, in addition to washing my hands in every separate work area. But I soon discovered that the place was a quality nightmare.

Customers included Parke-Davis, Johnson & Johnson, and many others. Johnson & Johnson used the capsules for its Tylenol® products. Later that first year, Tylenol was pulled from store shelves in a contamination scare and Greenwood was devastated—Tylenol capsules accounted for one-third of its output. But better days for the company were ahead.

The Greenwood plant ran 365 days a year on three shifts. It started by melting gelatin in hot water, and then adding dyes to match whatever color the customer wanted. The key to success was the consistency of the gelatin and dye, blended at just the right temperature to achieve a precise viscosity. But there was no verification of the quality of the gelatin and dye, and process control was minimal. The blended gelatin was then sent directly to the 40 capsule making machines, which had been designed in Detroit by Parke-Davis in the early 1900s. Each machine on a good day would produce some 600,000 capsules, or almost 24,000,000 per day for the entire 40-machine plant. The day's production would be sent to an outside warehouse for storage.

Since the plant didn't really have its manufacturing processes under control, and the process was not straight-through/continuous, inspection was relied on to weed out the bad capsules. The warehouse was stuffed with product awaiting inspection. I asked my hosts about the types of defects found with the capsules. So they showed me a wall chart, where it said they could have 15 unique defects. Judas Priest! That was impressive.

Then there was the ultimate shock. There were 120 full-time inspectors, 40 on each of three shifts, who were supposed to look for and sort out capsules with these 15 defects. They took me down to the inspection area, where 40 people on that particular shift were watching capsules zoom by on a conveyor at the rate of 25,000 per hour. These poor souls were supposed to spot and remove defective capsules at that rate. Impossible! It was a system of 100-percent inspection. It was imperative that these inspectors not be color-blind, because a so-called foreign capsule (one with a different color from the rest of the batch) must be identified at that dizzying rate. If they spotted a foreign capsule, the entire production batch was destroyed. Further, the operators could not be far-sighted, because then they wouldn't see any defects at all. Kidding aside, it was immediately plain to me that their chance of getting rid of all the defects was zero. Production lead time also was horrible. It took nearly six months to fill an order.

Not surprisingly, Capsugel was losing business. Its 35 percent share of the gelatin capsule market was slipping fast. I also learned that the company's foreign plants had similar problems. I decided to take Capsugel on. But where do you start?

We considered setting up statistical process control (SPC) systems. The U.S. auto industry was beginning to buzz at that time over SPC, where machine operators regularly measure samples of whatever they're making and keep a running total of results so that they can tell immediately when something is starting to drift out of specification. But we had to shelve that idea. What good is it to measure and chart product dimensions and specifications off one machine or 40 when you know that the raw materials and basic processes you're using are totally out of whack? Before we could put SPC on any machine making more than half a million capsules a day, I had to make sure that all the raw materials going into the process were of acceptable quality. Later I would get into an argument with W. Edwards Deming, the famous SPC guru, about this very point. There will be more about that in a minute.

The lack of process control led us in a different direction. We decided to set up process teams, with each looking at a discrete process problem. Obviously, we started at the beginning—the dyes and gelatin the plant received from suppliers. We were blessed that the plant had a superb quality statistician named Richard Anderson who set up training sessions for groups of highly qualified salaried and hourly workers. At the time of this writing, Anderson had just retired, and they're going to miss him more than anybody on earth. Week after week these teams would meet to define and solve the causes of their problems. Within three months, the quality of the gelatin was stabilized. The worst suppliers were dropped, and the good ones doubled their business. Controlling the quality of dyes was more difficult, but the teams were able to get significant positive results. Now, if they could get the gelatin viscosity perfect, and the dye color perfect, good things would happen.

When the teams had stabilized the gelatin production process, the capsule machines gradually began to improve their output. But this was just the beginning. Over time, the team system was expanded until people were taking a deep dive into every manufacturing process in the plant, all the way up to printing the doodads that you see on all gel capsules. As the improvement process continued, the results were published for all Capsugel plants worldwide. These plants copied the team approach. Fortunately, this data could be easily shared because of just one factor—all of the company's facilities worldwide had common manufacturing processes. Today, I want to shout that word: *COMMON*. Toyota and Honda are winning today because they have it.

I'd like to be able to say that we eliminated those 120 inspectors at Greenwood immediately. Dream on. It took years and a long list of process improvements to get to where they are now. Today, an inspector takes a small sample from each capsule-filled drum to verify quality. The last I heard, output per machine at Greenwood was 300 percent greater than when we started out. Lead time from order processing to delivery fell from six months to a matter of weeks, and produced very happy customers. All of this drove a huge increase in market share for the company, and I can only assume in profits as well. I heard that Capsugel was the most profitable unit of Warner-Lambert when it was sold to Pfizer. Profit, incidentally, was the one thing we never measured!

Still, I can't claim that Capsugel was a success because of me. It was mostly due to the open-minded management of the plant. This started with the plant manager, Chuck Hoover, who would become the division president and who recognized that quality and productivity go hand-in-hand and are the secret to success. In fact, the Capsugel Division established a new name for its quality and productivity effort—"qualitivity." The rest was based on a bunch of excellent engineers, the youngest group of engineers you ever saw in your life; most were from Clemson University. You couldn't believe what those kids did. Just recently I had a chance to return to Greenwood, about 25 years after my first visit. The company now has 70 of those 1916-vintage, high-tech machines, still working 365 days per year, and still pumping out millions of high-quality capsules. One of the kids on the first team I ever worked with is now president of the division.

What we learned at Capsugel was that quality is not a one-time event, but a matter of daily vigilance and continuous improvement. You never accept that today's quality and productivity level is the best you can achieve.

Capsugel was just a start. After we got that going, the corporate manufacturing folks at Warner-Lambert heard about it and called us up to take a look at their consumer products manufacturing. We started going up to Morris Plains, New Jersey. After landing at Newark, a big limousine would be waiting to take us to headquarters, where we were introduced to other products, including Dentyne® gum and Chiclets®.

Listerine® was an interesting one. We spent two or three days in the Listerine plant. It is packaged in a variety of bottle sizes, and that process was fairly easy. Wash the bottles, mix booze with water (yes, Listerine is part alcohol), add a flavor, bottle it, put on the cap, and add the label. But the plant had a problem—the labels were always crooked. It sounds silly, but customers complained about it, just as they would if the logo on their Cadillac® had been mounted at a 20-degree angle. We helped them design a process to straighten out the labels.

One day I was speaking to a group of workers in the auditorium of the Morris Plains headquarters. In the first row, right in front of me, were several young ladies and young gentlemen. I was talking about quality, and I had a bottle of Listerine in each hand, and

I wanted to show the workers how the labels were coming out crooked. I held out the two bottles and then put them together in front of me—and they both shattered! The poor folks who were sitting in the front row got drenched with Listerine and had to leave. What an embarrassment! But we soldiered on.

We also spent a serious amount of time at the Schick® razor plants in Europe and the U.S. The key to razor-blade quality is not just the quality of steel used. It also depends on various blade-grinding processes; and problems also arose in mounting the razors into the many containers that appeared on store shelves.

Then finally we got into pharmaceuticals. These were extremely challenging products. Every formulation has a specific shelf life once it is initially mixed. Therefore, you would ideally want to use a straight-through production process. In other words, once it is started in production, don't stop it and don't store it; just keep it moving. But that's not what we found. Take a look at how the industry worked:

- Raw materials were set up in a mixing or blending clean room. These ingredients had all been approved by the quality assurance department.

- The blended products were then stored in a quality control guarantee area where they invariably sat for days or weeks awaiting testing and approval by the quality assurance department.

- Next, the blended product was put into a capsule or made into a pill. There was no reason why this operation couldn't proceed immediately after approval by quality assurance. But most likely it would have to wait for the pill-making machine and the room that houses it to be cleaned and approved by the quality assurance department.

- Once the pill or capsule was made, it again would be stored for days or, most likely, weeks awaiting testing and approval by quality assurance.

- Now capsules were sent for packing in blister packs or to filling machines. Then they went into storage again for more quality control checks. Pharmaceuticals that were made into pills then received a tasty candy-type coating. Then they sat down again waiting for quality assurance testing.

- No, it wasn't over yet. After packaging, they again sat and waited. By now you can guess what for: quality control testing.

So, from the delivery of raw materials through the manufacturing process and out the door to the customer took a full three to six months. If you don't think this was a problem, just ask any pharmaceutical company CFO who had to find money to fund the inventories. Did this snail-like system change? You can bet on that.

First, the quality assurance tests were only performed after blending, coating, and packaging. Second, quality assurance was set up to start testing within a specific time period, which meant that two shifts of testing were used instead of just the day shift. Third, clean rooms for making pills and capsule-filling machines were scheduled to be cleaned and ready for production on a specific day and time. Total time from the receipt of raw materials to product shipping declined to less than one month.

Warner-Lambert was only the start of our pharmaceutical consulting business, which continued to prosper. We would gradually work with some of the premier companies in the business. As we traveled the world, we found that many other companies and plants were taking months to process prescription pharmaceuticals. Companies assumed that manufacturing processes fundamentally were not capable. Therefore, they thought, extensive inspection and testing was necessary. But slowly, pill by pill, these manufacturing processes were qualified. In other words, the companies began to gain confidence in them. Considerable in-process testing was eliminated, but still the final products met all Food & Drug Administration specifications. Lead time often was reduced to weeks, not months.

The pharmaceutical work kept us rolling because I still wasn't doing much in the automotive industry. By now, my sons Ron and

Ken were working for me. Ken is the engineer and Ron is the business guy. We had a ball. In particular, we came to understand fully that other manufacturing industries had problems similar to the auto industry.

One of our clients was a manufacturer of funeral caskets. This is a peculiar industry in that it doesn't operate factories on a just-in-time parts delivery schedule. The entire focus is to build thousands of caskets in steel, bronze, copper, and wood, and store them in numerous warehouses so that your specific casket request is available when you die. Good Lord, what if you were to have to wait two or three days lying on a mortuary table? But how does a casket differ from a car? Not at all, surprisingly.

First, the casket manufacturing plant stamped out the body (if I may use that word) in bronze, steel, or copper in large lot sizes. It seemed that it took workers forever to change dies in the presses, a familiar sight to us by this time. Next, they welded the stamped panels into a casket in a process similar to making car bodies. Finally, they ran the steel caskets through a paint system and then to an assembly line. Meanwhile, the plant's trim shop was sewing the interior trim, just as is done in making car seats. On the assembly line, springs, mattress, soft trim, and exterior hardware were installed. So far, this was just like automobile manufacturing, minus the engine, transmission, chassis, muffler, and catalytic converter. We've talked a lot about commonality, and the casket manufacturers are strictly focused on having a common product—they are all 6 ft (1.8 m) long. (Believe me, you don't want to know what happens to that 7 ft [2.1 m] basketball player!)

Our consulting work followed a pattern, at least in the beginning. Whenever we had a call from a company that needed help, it was my job to go. Sometimes Ron and Ken would go with me. Not all our clients were manufacturing companies. We did a lot of work for a car dealership in Minnesota, for instance. But when a factory called for help, I'd go and walk the plant floor until I got a good sense of what was wrong. Then I'd put a proposal together tailored to that client, and we would spend whatever time was necessary at the facility to turn things around. We didn't always get hired.

In 1983, GM announced Buick City, a plan to set up an efficient car manufacturing operation in Flint, Michigan. It was a play on Toyota City, which had become famous as the home in and around Nagoya, Japan, of the major manufacturing operations of Toyota and its group. One of the big efforts at Buick City was to get a fast and lean just-in-time parts inventory system going, like Toyota had in Nagoya. GM wanted somebody to review the plans and make a proposal for consulting work. I went up to Flint and spent considerable time there.

One of the things that impressed me most was the space set aside for about 50 repair booths at the end of the assembly line. This was not like Toyota at all. I went home and wrote up a 10-page assessment for GM, which essentially said that the plan wouldn't work. If you set aside 50 repair booths, instead of emphasizing first-time quality, you were guaranteeing that the booths would always be filled. That wasn't what GM wanted to hear, so naturally I didn't get the job. By 1999, Buick City was a ghost town.

One of our most exciting consulting assignments was working with an Austrian businessman I met at a BMW supplier conference on Hilton Head Island. His name was Karl Richter. He and his partners had developed the technology to make lumbar supports for automobile seats. Working in a tiny plant in Windsor, Ontario, he was just beginning to sell his products to domestic automakers. His company, Schukra of North America, had annual sales of just $5 million, mostly to makers of luxury cars. But he had an ambitious goal that was really a long-term strategic plan—to have a set of Schukra lumbar supports in every car and truck built worldwide.

Richter was intensely focused on his customer, meaning the auto industry worldwide and its broad range of cars and trucks. What did automotive manufacturers want? What technology was needed to meet that demand? And, how did Schukra plan to fulfill those requirements?

Initially, Schukra built manually operated lumbar supports— you may remember the kind that you cranked with a knob and adjusted against your back. But as the market for luxury cars and trucks exploded, the company developed two-way power and then four-way power lumbar supports. This drove a major plant expansion. Then the company developed technology for a massage lumbar, and automakers began putting them in passenger seats. Sales volume went even higher, creating the need for an all-new manufacturing plant in Windsor.

North America was not the only market. Lumbar applications were growing in Europe and Asia. Richter expanded in Europe and established joint ventures in the Far East. Sales grew to $40 million, then $100 million, and most recently $400 million. We helped with development of manufacturing processes and a strategic plan. But Schukra's success was really based on the intensity of the company's focus on the customer, its products and technology, quality, productivity, and low cost. The company's plants are models of lean manufacturing.

Karl always started his day when most people were still in bed, and usually he would still be at work after 7 p.m. He spent enormous amounts of time with customers and a great deal of each day was focused on operating details.

Schukra eventually was sold, but not until it was the world's No. 1 supplier of lumbar supports and, more importantly, a thoroughly competitive company.

More auto industry business began to come along. It was while consulting at an automatic transmission manufacturing plant that I had my so-called controversy with W. Edwards Deming. It was written up in the press at the time, so I might as well talk about it.

The plant had a major problem with the valve bodies that control the entire shifting functions of the automatic transmission. If you've never seen one of these, take my word that they're incredibly complex. The valve body defect rate was in the high 30-percent range.

Deming was also consulting at the plant, and I had never met him face to face until this day. He had become a demigod in Japan by teaching statistical process control, which as I said involves constant sampling and measuring of machined parts so that you can spot immediately if the process is drifting out of kilter. Every year in Japan since 1950, they had awarded the Deming Prize to companies showing big quality improvements.

There were at least 40 moving parts inside the main valve body, which was a highly machined casting. The machining process had to be perfect, since tolerances were required within microns. Deming's focus was to perfect the machining process. I didn't disagree with that. But the valves that went into the valve body were all coming from outside suppliers, and a full 40 percent of them were clear junk. Deming was urging the plant officials that first of all they had to get control of their basic processes. And I have a major problem with that. If all you're doing is measuring the machined product, and not paying attention to the quality of incoming material and parts, then theoretically each product will measure perfectly before it goes into the scrap heap.

So, this plant in the following weeks sent teams to all outside suppliers to get better incoming quality. Some months later the valve body defect rates had dropped to an insignificant number.

I think Deming and I both learned a lesson here. We had gotten into a very difficult conversation, but we didn't have a war over it. He and I both had one thing in common. He loved being on the plant floor, and so did I. He did a lot for the U.S. auto industry. Ford practically married him—for a while he was their main man. They didn't listen to him, but they married him.

One day in mid-1985, we learned that *Fortune* magazine planned to do a story on the manufacturing turnaround at Warner-Lambert and Harbour & Associates' role in it (Flax 1985). The story came out fine—quite positive, in fact. But I had mixed feelings about this part of it:

> *"The man who arrived surprised Bodenmann. Warner-Lambert is used to the standard-model, polished and pin-striped consultant. That's not how Harbour, 57, comes across. Success hasn't done much for his wardrobe, or altered his nerdy fifties haircut. He is raw-boned and long-limbed, angular and*

awkward, with a long, almost mournful face that would look as if it came from a medieval tapestry except for the cheap cigar often plugged into it. His speech can be combustible."

Well, I don't smoke *cheap* cigars. Otherwise, I'd have to admit that's still my way.

REFERENCE

Flax, Steven. 1985. "An Auto Man Tunes Up Warner-Lambert." *Fortune*, March 4.

Chapter 7

GM's Most Dangerous Decade

"Our biggest challenge is that we're having to change the mindset of literally hundreds of thousands of people, from the guy who's just been hired in one of our assembly plants right on through to the top echelon—not only our organization, but our suppliers as well."
—Lloyd Reuss, general manager of Buick Division,
March 1982

"We had a whole new workforce, a whole new plant, a whole new product, plus every kind of new manufacturing technology you could think of. It was more than we could handle."
—Larry Tibbets, plant manager,
GM Hamtramck Assembly Plant,
January 1990

My business was starting to pick up nicely, but I can't say the same for General Motors Corp. About this time, in the early to mid-1980s, it was becoming increasingly obvious that GM had put itself on a path toward self-destruction. Strategic blunders were enormous: a disastrous 1984 corporate reorganization, a new multi-billion-dollar Saturn® project that never fulfilled its original promise, and a plan to spend tens of billions of dollars on advanced automation, which often had to be scrapped. The common flaw in these, excuse me, was that they abandoned the C-word: common. Together, they set GM's competitive drive back by about 15 years, and opened the door wide for Japanese automakers to get firmly established in the North American market.

To understand how such a thing could happen, you have to remember what GM was like circa 1981, when Roger Smith and Jim McDonald began their 10-year reign, respectively, as

GM chairman and president. I've already talked about how GM executives bristled when I suggested at the meeting in New York that they were about to get their butts kicked by Toyota. Their deep denial was understandable. Since the 1920s, GM had been an unbeatable powerhouse. It was the world's largest industrial concern, and by far the richest among the globe's auto companies. An entire generation of GM executives grew up believing that whatever the company did was right by definition, since GM was doing it. And whatever the company did was strictly first class. If GM built a new assembly plant, it would have to be able to withstand an H-bomb blast. If the competition came up with something interesting, no problem, GM would just leapfrog them—do something 10 times as good.

In 1979, GM had 47 percent of the U.S. light truck market and 46 percent of the passenger car market. There were no Japanese manufacturers producing cars in North America. It took GM 35–45 man-hours to assemble a vehicle that had on average 7.4 defects as it left the factory. Toyota required about 15 man-hours to assemble one of its small cars. When Roger Smith retired on August 1, 1990, he assured everybody that the company's competitiveness was at an all-time high—even though its U.S. market share was now down to 37 percent. (As of this writing, GM held just 21.4 percent of the U.S. market.) The main cause of that 10-point market share loss in the 1980s, and much of the decline that followed, was the 1984 corporate tear-up that split North American operations into two groups: CPC (Chevrolet-Pontiac-Canada) and BOC (Buick-Oldsmobile-Cadillac). Somewhat earlier, GM had split off many of its truck operations into the Truck & Bus Group. But CPC and BOC were the main culprits here.

I've already mentioned how some top executives at GM were aware of the growing competitive threat. In addition, outside studies pointed to problems in the way GM developed vehicles, usually with so many late engineering changes that it was tough to have a clean new vehicle launch. By the time Smith and McDonald took over, it was apparent that something had to be done. After all, GM still operated much as it had in the 1920s, with a whole host of independent kingdoms calling their own shots. The head of Chevrolet Division, for instance, ran a manufacturing empire as well as a product engineering and market operation, and if what he wanted conflicted with something Pontiac was doing, so be it. This had worked well when there was no external competition.

GM's head office served essentially as a big bank, handing out capital to the car divisions and internal parts manufacturers. It demanded a certain return on that investment, no questions asked. Clearly, it was time to move to centralized product development, engineering, manufacturing, purchasing, and marketing. If GM had done that, the story of the 1980s probably would have been different. But the company choked at taking such a big leap all at once. Instead, it took an intermediate step, carving itself up into the two car divisions. This destroyed the main thing that had given GM its strength: supreme manufacturing capability based entirely on the ethic of "common."

In the 1970s and early 1980s, the company's manufacturing structure included General Motors Assembly Division (GMAD). It managed all the assembly plants except the so-called home plants, which were still tied to the car divisions. These old home plants were rooted in GM history: Buick in Flint, Oldsmobile in Lansing, Pontiac in Pontiac. The second largest manufacturing operation within GM was the Fisher Body Division. This division was responsible for more than just the production of car and truck bodies: for instance, there were plants that made seats and instrument panels. But Fisher Body's main focus was to stamp major body panels and weld them into a finished body. These two processes had grown inefficient over the years and allowed quality to lapse. But the division still had some strengths, which could have been honed to a much sharper edge. Over the years, for instance, it had:

- A common body architecture; every vehicle body was designed to be welded using exactly the same process.
- There were common die designs for major body panels such as doors, hoods, and roofs, considerably cutting die design and construction costs.

- Body welding was totally common using available technology.
- Processes at the assembly plants were totally common, meaning that components were always added to the vehicle at the same workstation regardless of the platform.

But these were some of the problems at Fisher Body:

- Press lines making major body panels that were engineered to run 10 or 15 strokes per minute or 600 to 900 per hour were only running at 50–60 percent of their capabilities.
- Die changes from one body panel to another took 4–6 hours or even as much as 24 hours, while Japanese competitors only needed 5–10 minutes.
- Once dies were set, die repair operators would work under the ram of the press to ensure a quality part, interrupting production. Their Japanese counterparts would fix every die that needed repair between production runs, so no production time was lost.
- Die construction and design was always based on maximum structure and weight to prevent breakage, simply because the press lines were not maintained properly. In other words, the tools were more massive than they really needed to be. Press line preventive maintenance was not a focus. You run the press until it breaks; then you fix it.
- The quality of incoming steel was uneven. Repair work was considered normal. There were squads of rework operators and scrap was significant.

GM could have, should have, set quality and productivity goals for these operations and charted a course of specific action to address its lack of competitiveness. Instead, GMAD and Fisher Body were abolished, along with the engine and transmission manufacturing divisions. The three main operating groups, CPC, BOC, and Truck & Bus would each have their own assembly plants, body stamping plants, engine plants, and transmission plants. They were also assigned separate manufacturing engineering, product design, and product engineering operations. Other new conglomerations of the former GM also had been created, including Fisher Guide to make lighting and interior trim, Packard Electric for wire harnesses, Delco Remy for electrical components, and others.

The transition was a nightmare. You can just imagine what the first staff meetings were like when thousands of GM engineers, designers, and managers eventually discovered where they were supposed to sit. I remember a top-level BOC official describing to me what the scene was like.

"There were 40 guys in there, all new faces. They introduced the new head of manufacturing. The question on everyone's mind was, 'Where did you come from?'"

"'I'm from stamping,' he said.

"Everyone is thinking, 'Well, now you've got 16 assembly plants, don't you? Yeah, that's right. What do you know about assembly? Nothing! What do you know about powertrains? Even less!'"

The common focus was not just gone, it was now considered undesirable. Competition between the groups would be "good."

I personally watched in horror as BOC and CPC created all new systems and standards. They did not, would not, talk to each other. When each group started designing new cars and trucks, the common focus for body architecture, assembly processing, and body welding all went out the window. This meant that a car built in a CPC plant could not be built in a BOC plant. Each group would design and build its own engines and automatic transmissions, another major disaster. Managers from GMAD and Fisher Body were sent in all directions, and GM now had:

- unique body designs and architecture,
- unique body welding facilities,
- unique paint processing,
- unique assembly line processing,
- unique die and tooling designs,
- unique stamping processing, and
- absolutely no operating flexibility.

That wasn't the end.

GM had entered the 1980s with a lot of money in the bank. The company was using it to build a new set of Leviathan assembly plants, equipping them with leading-edge (read: unproven) manufacturing technology. The footprint of each of these new plants—in Oklahoma City, Oklahoma; Orion Township, Michigan; Wentzville, Missouri; and Hamtramck, Michigan—was an enormous 3.2 million ft^2 (297,280 m^2), enough to cover three baseball parks. Much of that space was dedicated to parts storage, at a time when the auto industry was moving to just-in-time parts delivery systems.

GM bragged that it would have 14,000 robots in operation in all its plants, a goal that at best was technology for technology's sake. Much of this technology eventually had to be scrapped long before its theoretical working life was over. The main problem was that these plants were tooled for only one product. There was zero flexibility, in other words, at a cost of $700 million to $800 million for each plant. Worse, they were largely manned using the same set of unproductive UAW work rules and standards as the older factories they replaced. As late as 1994, Hamtramck required 4,200 workers for 912 cars per day or 39 hours per vehicle. Oklahoma City, making 1,024 cars per day, was down to 3,850 workers but was still at 30 hours per car. Orion Township made 1,040 cars per day with 4,700 workers or 36 hours per car.

What was the return on that $800 million tooling investment per assembly plant? You have to wonder, where was the GM board of directors while all of this was going on? What questions did they ask? Perhaps they felt overwhelmed because more boondoggles were in the works.

As part of the reorganization, GM decided to modernize all of its 17 major stamping plants. The company committed to buy some 106 new transfer presses, the latest in metal stamping technology. The total investment would exceed $1.4 billion, with the largest transfer press lines costing $30 million each. At the time, GM had almost 440 conventional "tandem" press lines. The transfer presses were far more automated, flexible, and computer controlled and, on paper, far more productive than the old technology. Each new line had the capacity to replace two of the old ones. But that's not how it worked out. GM's metal stamping engineers should have visited Warner-Lambert's Capsugel plants, where continuous modernization of 1916-vintage technology and attention to quality/productivity goals had boosted capsule output from 600,000 per day per machine to over 2.4 million. GM's technical staffers had not done their homework. The new presses they bought would use old dies, old die designs, old part processing methods, and the same tired old UAW work rules. It would take years for GM to sort out this mess. The message here is that you shouldn't buy new technology unless you've mastered the old.

And then, in the midst of all this, came Saturn. This was GM's attempt to build a small car in the U.S. to compete in quality and production cost with Toyota. Certainly a laudable goal, but one that smacked of GM's old hubris: we'll leapfrog them. It started with a clean sheet of paper; an all-new car design including engine and transmission, all-new manufacturing plant, new technologies, a radically new working agreement with the UAW, a new marketing emphasis, and a new dealer network. And what a manufacturing complex it was! Plunked down in the middle of a Tennessee farm field, it included vehicle assembly, metal stamping, plastics fabrication, engine assembly, transmission assembly, aluminum die casting using an all-new "lost foam" process, and a variety of machining operations, all of it connected and intimately synchronized. Hell, there was even a gift shop. For GM to assemble the talent to design and build all of this was a huge undertaking. Finding the manufacturing expertise to carry it all out was just about impossible.

There's an old adage in the auto industry: never do an "all new." This is one of the secrets of the Japanese system. You never, ever see "all new" at Honda, Nissan, or Toyota. Now, they might have an all-new car, but the plant, people, and processing are all the same. They have built new plants in the U.S. and Canada, but loaded them with proven tooling and existing vehicle designs.

GM, in its heydays of the 1950s and 1960s, rarely did anything all new. The standard Chevrolet car, for instance, had a new body in 1955, 1957, 1959, and 1962. The 1958 model was mostly new, but the others borrowed extensively from existing parts and components. Saturn, in fact, wasn't GM's first attempt to make a competitive small car with the all-new ethic. Remember the Chevrolet Vega? Built at a new plant in Lordstown, Ohio, it was another quality and productivity disaster.

In retrospect, GM should have focused its drive to boost small car manufacturing on Chevrolet instead of Saturn. Chevrolet dealers howled when they found out about Saturn, because it was a new brand right in the middle of their market. In any case, Saturn struggled along, I assume losing billions and billions of dollars. Finally, GM pulled the plug and created the Saturn you see today, with cars and sport utility vehicles (SUVs) sharing platforms with other GM models and assembled in other plants. The goal of beating Japan on productivity and quality in small car production was ditched long ago, unfulfilled, and the manufacturing complex in Spring Hill, Tennessee stands half-empty.

Unexpectedly, Harbour & Associates was given the chance to watch what was happening at GM from the inside. As I said earlier, we had been shut out of GM. But one day we got a surprise call from Dennis Pawley, the young plant manager of the Fiero® assembly plant in Pontiac. Pawley was one of those guys with manufacturing in his blood; he was dynamic and destined for success. He eventually left GM to help Mazda establish its assembly plant south of Detroit. He then moved to United Technologies, and later became executive vice president of manufacturing at Chrysler.

The Fiero had an odd birth. Since the 1950s, Pontiac had lusted to produce a two-seat sports car. But the corporation had always squelched the idea. It didn't want any internal competition for the Chevrolet Corvette®. But in the oil shock of 1979–81, Pontiac officials were able to sell top executives on the idea of a fuel-efficient, two-seat commuter car—even though they really hoped eventually to turn it into a high-performance machine.

The central office sent down one caveat—the Fiero couldn't use any new major components. Engines, transmission, brakes, etc., had to come from the existing parts bin. But it was innovative in one way. Like the Saturn vehicle, it had a body made of plastic panels fixed to a steel space frame. And it too was fraught with quality problems. Early production cars had one of the worst problems possible: engine compartment fires.

Pawley asked us to take a look. We teamed with plant supervision and hourly workers for several weeks just to identify the problems, let alone the causes. Of course, the most pronounced problem was an old story—the product engineers had just thrown the design over the proverbial office wall to the manufacturing engineers, with the familiar "Here it is, go build it." Then, while the manufacturing systems were being set up and tested, late engineering changes came down frequently. We found significant problems:

- It was difficult to build the space frames with exact tolerances and repeatability. When the plastic body panels were installed, there often were huge gaps between panels.

- Painting the plastic panels took an enormous effort. Less than half of the vehicles made it through the paint shop with an acceptable finish. The rest had to be repaired and repainted. That required a considerable inspection/repair workforce.

- Assembly line workers had endless trouble installing the body panels, and parts shortages frequently disrupted the work flow.

Slowly, these problems were identified and the causes addressed. It was a daunting effort, involving numerous meetings with product engineers to address critical design issues. The plant's quality eventually improved, but never to the level of the Japanese competition. Pontiac finally got something like its dream of a true sports car when the Fiero GT with a V-6 engine arrived, but by then it was time to pull the plug on the whole program.

Then we were hired to help BOC do a major study comparing its operations with the Japanese. It was quite an effort, extending over two years, and involved both BOC management and local UAW officials. Joint teams looked at everything: assembly quality, the whole issue of complexity, productivity, tooling, facilities, paint systems, the way assembly lines were manned and balanced, and supplier quality. But some things were left out. There was no attempt to highlight design and product engineering problems. And we were specifically forbidden even to mention union-related production issues like pay and benefits, nonworking union reps, Byzantine job classifications, and outsourcing. This was at a time when GM thought its best stance toward the union was to try to enlist it as a partner, and any negative talk was a no-no. There were teams in every plant looking at the list of politically correct issues.

Every month we had large central meetings where a team would present its findings, and these would be shared with every other BOC plant. We could never get a product engineer to come to these meetings. And the sharing process was negated by the fact that the plants had little in common, process-wise. The body shops were all different; each paint shop was unique; and the assembly lines had been laid out by different sets of engineers. For example, the air conditioning unit was assembled in station 40 in one plant, station 62 in another, and station 88 in another. What a disaster!

One day, toward the end of the second year of our consulting contract, I brought the process to a screeching halt. It was at one of the monthly sessions where I got up and said, "Gentlemen, it's time to discuss this other thing—the uncompetitive labor agreement with the UAW." Management just exploded. They tore me apart, and called a halt to the meeting. But I wasn't going to let this thing linger. We were just floundering because nobody wanted to get at it. But you couldn't just leave it like that in a hole in the floor. It had to come up to the table some time. This was in stark contrast to working at pharmaceutical companies, where every quality and productivity issue was fair game.

I remember an interesting conversation with Bob Truxell, who ran GM's Truck & Bus Group until 1983, when he went over to General Dynamics Land Systems Division (LSD) as general manager. LSD at that time made the Abrams M-1 main battle tank at a plant in Warren, Michigan. His first week on the job there he called his staff together and said, "Fill me in on the company." And so, all of the executives came out; they went into a big boardroom and handed him a strategic plan. Here was a thick, comprehensive document that covered everything: cost, quality, production, productivity, and design; every piece of the company and its business was detailed. They knew who the competition was, what the competitions' strengths and weaknesses were, what LSD's strengths and weaknesses were, and the path that had to be followed to reach the company's goals. He was blown away. At Truck & Bus he had asked for a strategic plan and what they had given him was a piece of crap in comparison. He said, "I'm a dummy compared to these guys. At GM we never got direction like this." And in fact, the domestic auto industry had no comprehensive strategic plan for decades. If I go to Toyota or Honda, they have strategic plans built on a lot of formulas like, "What do we need in design and manufacturing engineering, sales, and marketing?"

One of the oddest parts of this whole saga is that Ford watched what GM was doing and, instead of rejoicing at all the waste, went stumbling down the same road. You had to be insane to follow what GM was doing. But in 1994, Ford announced the Ford 2000 initiative, which split the company into five groups, each in charge of designing and building vehicles for the entire world in different segments. This was at least an advance on GM's 1984 reorganization, in that there should have been more commonality within discrete product lines: small cars, for instance. But it didn't work out very well. Today, Ford is still stuck with a system of unique, inflexible plants at a time when it needs just the opposite.

I said earlier that Ford was the only one of the Big Three that agreed with my conclusions about Toyota and the Japanese productivity advantage at the onset. Ford executives showed me the studies they had done. The stamping guy who had been part of the Ford team would say something like, "In the Japanese systems everything is common." The assembly guy would say the same thing, almost as an offhand remark. But "common" was never highlighted. So, Ford had a chance from the beginning to get to work on that, but it went right over management's heads. They never applied it.

The year 1994 also marked the beginning of a major turn-around for GM. Under North American Chief Rick Wagoner, the company began to unravel the CPC/BOC mess and started down a new path toward continuous improvement. I believe Harbour & Associates had something to do with that.

Chapter 8

The Japanese in North America

*"If we cannot succeed in California, it is unlikely
that we can succeed elsewhere in the U.S."
—Shoichiro Toyoda, president,
Toyota Motor Corp., March 21, 1982*

*"The real problem is that the U.S. car industry went to sleep for
20 years. It was a gentleman's market, like a tennis match.
Well, it's more like a fight out behind the bar now."
—Harold Sperlich, president,
Chrysler Corp., February 1983*

Ever cautious, Toyota waited three years from my visit there
with the Arthur D. Little team before making a move toward assembling cars in the U.S. And then, it was a half-step.

Early in 1983, Toyota and GM agreed to form a joint venture
to build cars at a plant in Fremont, California, which GM had
permanently closed the previous year. The company was named
New United Motor Manufacturing, Inc., and immediately became
universally known as NUMMI.

Toyota knew sooner or later it had to start producing cars
in the U.S. Honda and Nissan were already here. Trade friction
was running high, and that might get worse if the company simply continued to export vehicles from Japan. Politically, it was
necessary to make a greater contribution to the U.S. economy
by hiring workers and buying parts here. That would disarm the
protectionists, who were clamoring for import quotas, local content
requirements, and higher tariffs. Toyota also realized that, over
the longer term, the company would make more money by building cars and trucks here instead of just exporting from Japan. A

North American manufacturing base would insulate the company from volatile changes in international currency exchange rates at a time when the yen had begun an historic rise against the dollar that progressively inflated the U.S. price of Japanese-built goods. A joint venture would also give Toyota a relatively low-risk forum to try its luck with U.S. parts suppliers and confront the thing it feared most: the U.S. worker. At Fremont, it got the second wish in spades. When it closed in 1982, the GM plant had a typically fractious workforce, the usual management-labor friction, burdensome work rules, and thousands of grievances.

GM saw the joint venture as a learning experience. The plant was somewhat co-managed, but the final decisions rested with the Japanese manufacturing people. GM could cycle managers in and out of NUMMI, where they would gain firsthand experience in the Toyota Production System and its application in America (and eventually in GM's European and other overseas operations as well). In fact, GM had begun to understand what we at Harbour & Associates knew well: *the secret to Japanese quality and productivity was not any one technique or technology, but an entire management system.* This was a new business model, if you will—one that was fundamentally different from the U.S. manufacturers. If you wanted to boil it down to a few words, you might say that the U.S. auto industry focused on earning a profit, while the Japanese dedicated themselves to winning customers and market share.

It helped that there was less pressure on Japanese companies to show a profit than in the U.S., where Wall Street ultimately ruled just about everything. And the Japanese had other major advantages as they built their market here:

- an extremely weak yen that boosted profits on Japan-built vehicles exported to the U.S.;

- a highly motivated workforce, with labor unions in Japan that, in general, didn't interfere with management decisions;

- a home market protected by numerous legal and informal barriers to sales of cars built in the U.S. and Europe;

- a keiretsu system that grouped automakers, automotive suppliers, and banks into families of companies that gave the automakers extremely low-cost capital and parts;

- a virtual partnership with the Japanese government that produced a beneficial trade and regulatory climate;

- an operating culture from the head office to the factory floor with a nearly religious devotion to manufacturing, design, product development, purchasing, and other disciplines ensuring high quality and manufacturing efficiency; and

- twin oil shocks in the 1970s that favored sales of their small, fuel-efficient cars and pickup trucks.

But at the end of the day, Toyota had to have more money coming in than going out, just like GM. And the way to do that, Toyota had discovered, was to tune its manufacturing systems to clockwork efficiency.

Honda was first to begin U.S. production in 1982 at its Marysville, Ohio plant. Nissan followed in 1983 in Smyrna, Tennessee. The first Chevrolet Nova from NUMMI rolled off the line in December, 1984. Mazda began production in 1987 at Flat Rock, Michigan. Toyota's first wholly owned plant began making the Camry® in Georgetown, Kentucky in 1988, the same year that Mitsubishi launched production in Normal, Illinois. Subaru and Isuzu also joined the party. Toyota and Honda continued to expand dramatically in the U.S. and Canada. Not surprisingly, the Toyota Production System and the Honda Way have become bywords for quality and productivity.

Success for the other Japanese makers in America has been uneven although, in general, they too have continued to grow as Detroit automakers declined. For every manufacturing job the Japanese have created in the U.S., the Detroit-based producers and their suppliers have lost three. That's because the Japanese are more efficient overall, and in the beginning they brought in major components like engines and transmissions from Japan. For example, Honda finds it more efficient to build its own major stamping dies and body shop facilities and tools rather than buy them from outside suppliers. Nissan, on the other hand, is a far greater fan of advanced automation and robotics than Toyota. However, despite differences in philosophy, our studies found a great deal of similarity across the group. The focus of these companies is very basic. They pay attention to every detail; never assume anything; and follow up relentlessly. "Very anal," as one American executive at a Japanese firm describes. They spend enormous amounts of time investigating what customers want and strive to give it to them. But they know a great design and a high-value product will only result from a set of tools, facilities, and people who can execute them. It sounds a bit too obvious, but you'd be surprised at the number of people working at U.S. auto companies who don't seem to understand that it's a hardware business.

For all of the Japanese, the product engineering and manufacturing watchword is "common." The term "unique" is just not in their vocabulary. Each of the Japanese companies starts with a common foundation—the body platform, or the basic metal structure that defines the car's length and width. Platforms for different cars have common architecture. This means that different cars on different platforms can be welded in one body shop using the same set of tools. Remember, a unique body shop for a plant assembling 1,000 cars per day costs $90 million to $100 million. Think of the difference in profitability of a company that can build two different vehicles in one plant at full capacity, while another company has to operate two plants at one-half capacity to get the same output because the body shops are unique! This is exactly how Honda can manufacture the Civic® and Accord® in the same plant using the same body and assembly lines. Common architecture also allows common paint shops and assembly workstations in all plants. Another huge benefit is that a technological change or a new productivity idea hatched at one plant can be easily and quickly applied to all the others.

A contrary example to all of this was Ford's Wixom, Michigan assembly plant, which closed permanently in 2007, and as of this writing is a candidate for demolition. At one time it had three unique platforms in production with three forms of body architecture designed by three separate engineering staffs . . . and zero flexibility. If you moved back up the production chain from body welding to metal stamping, the impact of the unique body architecture was just devastating. If you needed hoods or door panels for five different vehicles, then you had five unique die designs.

In the domestic industry, unique body architecture created such a demand for dies that they were being purchased from as far away as Brazil and even Japan. Japanese automakers took die design to its simplest form. Every part—hood, fender, body side, or whatever—would have a common design except, of course, for the sculptured surface. A particular die could be used in any press line of the same overall size, while the domestic companies could load their unique die in only one stamping press. So the Japanese could change dies that were common in less than 10 minutes, compared with the 4–6 hours it usually took a domestic automaker to change from production of one part to another. Domestic press lines would produce about 350 parts per hour, while Japanese competitors were making 600 per hour.

One day while we were doing the plant study for BOC, we met a great tool and die maker at the Kalamazoo plant named Warren Miller. Not long after, Honda contacted us and wanted help hiring a tool and die man for their stamping operations in Ohio.

"Go hire Warren Miller. He's a great guy," we said.

The Kalamazoo plant was getting ready to close, so Miller went down there for an interview. On his way home, he dropped by our office to say, "I got the job. I even got a raise! I don't believe this. I don't even have a college degree and they're making me supervisor of die construction." And he bragged, "I'm going to show these guys how to make a set of dies!"

Two years later he came to our office, eating crow. "I've never had an education like this in my life," he said. He had learned the Honda Way. He's now head of stamping for Chrysler LLC.

I've already said that a major part of the Japanese system is never to do everything entirely new. In moving to the U.S., they usually started out with a proven product and tooling. Of course, there was an all-new workforce, but another common trait of the Japanese was to make certain that the workers were selected and trained to fit their system. The system demanded that management was the only voice of authority in the plant. So, this ruled out hiring UAW workers (except for Mazda and Mitsubishi, which because of their ties with Ford and Chrysler, were forced to sign UAW agreements). But the system also demanded teamwork, and a willingness to accept responsibility for quality work and continuous improvement.

To fill 1,000 jobs, the Japanese companies would interview something like 15,000 people whose names were sifted from 50,000 job applications. In Japanese plants, everybody was on the same page. In America, the Japanese needed the same, and they were determined to get it. Pay and benefits were comparable to the UAW, so as not to give the union an easy road to organizing. The union did, however, show some flexibility in negotiating labor agreements at NUMMI and other Japanese-managed plants. For one thing, it was willing to give management a break on job classifications and work rules—among production workers if not skilled trades.

NUMMI quickly got its act together, and to this day it is doing well. GM sent salaried staff there from just about every discipline: product, manufacturing and quality engineering, materials management, and finance among them. After a tour of duty there, these staff members were assigned to other plants where they were expected to share their knowledge. Some of them became stars, like Tom LaSorda, now the No. 2 executive at Chrysler LLC. It's easy to second-guess from this distance, but I wish GM had done it differently. How much impact can one NUMMI-trained manager have in a plant full of people dedicated to doing things the old way? GM would have been much better off if it had concentrated them a little better. What if a single plant, say the Hamtramck assembly plant that makes the Cadillac®, had an entire NUMMI-trained management crew?

I hope this doesn't sound too negative. The Detroit automakers weren't stuck in neutral. Throughout the terrible 1980s and into the 1990s they had made steady improvements in quality and productivity. If they hadn't, they would have disappeared long ago. Nevertheless, a decade after my first report on Toyota, there was still a large gap between the Japanese and American groups. Not many people, and certainly not the general public, knew how large the disparity was—until we began publicly issuing annual reports on manufacturing efficiency.

Chapter 9

The *Harbour Report*

"When plants producing similar vehicles are compared to one another . . . workers in union plants assemble vehicles in fewer hours than their nonunion counterparts in 11 of 12 product categories. This performance, which is reported in the 'Harbour Report'—the most closely watched study of auto industry productivity—would not be possible if union contracts were a drag on productivity."
—*UAW white paper, 2007*

"We are all going to be a lot leaner. It isn't automatic that all the companies are going to be healthy. Those that can adapt are going to be strong and profitable."
—*Donald Petersen, president, Ford Motor Co., May 1982*

We had discovered that there was a market for information and expertise about manufacturing. This isn't surprising. The struggle to get more productive and improve quality was the No. 1 story of the domestic auto industry in the 1980s and 1990s. In addition, everybody was hungry for news about the competitive battle. Is GM gaining ground? Just how good is Honda? How on earth can Toyota keep winning like that; is it magic? And so on, endlessly. The news media wanted to know, and so did Wall Street and the whole investment community. Auto industry analysts at the big financial houses in New York knew next to nothing about the bones of manufacturing. They always had a hard time figuring out what was happening in the plants and what it meant. Finally, the auto companies themselves were always interested in news about their competitors. Most of them had some kind of intelligence-gathering operation, and there was always a leaky network of suppliers who, despite confidentiality agreements, would gossip about the competition. It's a deeply secretive industry, and there weren't many good, authoritative, publicly available sources of information about manufacturing issues.

The general public, of course, still doesn't care much about manufacturing per se. It's as if new cars are delivered to the dealership by the stork. The buyer doesn't say, "Wow, this car has 3,700 welds in the body and this other one only has 2,700." But Americans grew up with their fannies in car seats, and they can tell that there's a big difference in the way the car with 3,700 welds feels on the road compared with the other one. That's the critical manufacturing difference, and explains in a nutshell why the Japanese were winning.

We started Harbour & Associates with five people. I had two retired engineers from Chrysler who had worked for me along with a finance guy. My wife was our secretary; she typed up everything. In 1983, I hired my son Ron, and two years later my son Ken came aboard. Ken's an engineer, and he understood how to apply engineering for quality and productivity. Ron, a business major, was focused on results. I've mentioned that we did a lot of work in the pharmaceutical industry. Auto industry clients also came along. I worked with Schukra, the maker of automotive seat lumbar supports, and also with Budd Co. Budd was a major metal stamping company that also had a plastics division. We worked with other auto suppliers, and even car dealerships. We did a lot of work for Ford, some for Chrysler, and by the late 1980s we were invited to work for GM at the Fiero® plant, the BOC car group, and other places. We started hiring people, maybe two to three new faces per year.

I remember one time we got an invitation, "Would you please come to BMW? We want you to look at our manufacturing operations (in Germany) and tell us what you think." So we spent two weeks there. They weren't the most efficient outfit.

In the final meeting, when I presented my report, I cut them up a little bit. The top BMW guy got a little huffy and told the people at the meeting, "It's okay to listen to what Harbour says, but remember, we do things the BMW way." I got a call from them a couple of weeks later. "We would like Harbour & Associates to help us. But we don't want you. Send your sons Ron and Ken."

When the first *Harbour Report* came out early in 1981, I have to admit it was a bit crude. A college professor would have quoted hundreds of sources and included endless cross-references and footnotes. We were just direct and simple. But it was a monster in impact, as I've described. At Harbour & Associates we debated about whether it would be a one-time study, or whether we should continue to update, refine, and expand it. The latter is what we eventually decided to do. But at first, I wasn't convinced that this was something you should do every year. It gets redundant. The pace of change in the auto industry is slow, and you often can't make enough improvement in a year to show a difference in the overall productivity statistics.

We tried to get the Big Three to share their data with us, but they refused. They just were in no mood to show the whole world how they were doing, because they knew they'd suffer in the comparison.

We did updates sporadically between 1981 and 1989. In 1989, we collected all the studies over the past decade and put them into one package. That went over well. Then we talked about doing an annual public study, much the same as J.D. Power & Associates was doing annual surveys on customer perceptions of quality in the automobile industry and other businesses. It became quite an argument. At the beginning, I thought it would be a waste of time to do an annual study. Maybe every five years was a good time frame. In addition, we were busy. I had been spending less and less time on the *Harbour Report*, and more time zooming around the world on business with our clients. But my daughter Laurie, a business major, who had worked part time at Harbour & Associates while attending the University of Michigan and came on full time in 1988, started fighting with me. "This is an important study," she insisted. "Nothing else shows the public, including customers, lawmakers, and investors, what the heck is going on in America's most important industry," she said.

"Well, if it's so important, I'd like to have somebody in the industry tell me that," I said.

So we polled the auto manufacturers and got some interesting results. First of all, Chrysler said it would be interested in participating in an annual study. Ford said pretty much the same. We can see now that Ford really wasn't doing much at the time to transform its manufacturing operations. Sure, the company was talking a good game, all about putting in the new Ford Production System and so forth. Then GM came in and said, "We absolutely need this kind of study every year." The source of this enthusiasm was Rick Wagoner, a rising GM executive who was determined to whip the No. 1 automaker back into competitive shape after its drastic slide in the 1980s and early 1990s. I'll have a lot more to say about Wagoner in a minute. Then I was shocked when Toyota, Honda, and Nissan all said they would also welcome an annual study. The Japanese trio wanted to see how fast the domestic companies were gaining on them in productivity. That was good enough for me. Laurie was right, and we decided to go ahead with an annual study, not really knowing that it would become the Bible of manufacturing issues in the auto industry.

Every year, the report showed our interpretation of who had the most productive manufacturing and assembly operations among the U.S. producers. At first, we just used publicly available data—generally, the number of workers in a plant and the plant's output. When you're schooled in auto manufacturing, you can tell a lot just from those statistics. But admittedly, it doesn't tell the whole story. You can assume eight hours per shift per worker, and from that basis show how many hours it takes Company X to assemble a car, or an engine, or a transmission. The companies wouldn't give us their secret data on hours per car and the rest, because this included all the hours that we could only estimate: overtime hours for repair and maintenance, and the like. In other words, our reports showed them losing their fannies at eight hours, but in reality they had overtime coming out their eardrums! It was even worse than we said.

And so it was an annual fight. Finally, in the mid-1990s, Laurie and two other staffers we had hired from GM, Becky Lee and Patty Waters, went to all the manufacturers again and just put on a sales pitch. It's a great report, they said, but we're kidding ourselves that there's no overtime. Gradually and reluctantly, they all agreed to share their data with us. And then it became an even bigger bomb than when we started.

With the doors opening, Harbour & Associates staffers routinely began to visit 20–25 assembly, stamping, engine, and transmission plants each year. They verified our conclusions and came to fully understand the processes each plant was using. These visits also were rewarding for workers in the plants. Workers would make detailed presentations, almost always on the plant floor, where they discussed their problems, the cause of the problems they were attacking, and the results achieved.

We began getting mobs of reporters at the annual press conference where we announced the results. It was a shock to me. I never thought the day would come when we'd go to the Detroit Athletic Club, one of the favorite Detroit venues for press meetings, and have to stand up in front of more than 100 people. Here comes the *Wall Street Journal*, the *New York Times*, *Business Week*, *Newsweek*, the Detroit papers, television crews, dozens of trade publications, and news media from around the country. At first, I thought the press was overplaying it. But groups from the auto companies also attended, and after our presentation they usually handed out their own news releases in response to our numbers. Not surprisingly, the tone of these comments from the Detroit firms grew warmer year by year as we charted their improvements. Eventually even the UAW began to say good things about us.

I loved going out on our annual plant visits. But one of the most interesting parts of this process for me was the meetings we had with each of the manufacturers before we made the report public.

General Motors, whose management had initially been in denial about its problems, had gone full circle. Whenever we went to GM we'd get a crowd of people. Everybody who is anybody would be in that meeting, 30–40 people, and half of them standing. And you could smell the fact that we had put another bomb on the table, and that the people at GM were going to go after it. When we went to Chrysler, there was a lot of interest and a lot of people did a lot of good things. But at Ford it all fell on deaf ears. We would frequently not get the right people at the meeting. They'd dispute it and then forget it. The Japanese were always cordial. Toyota, Honda, and Nissan always listened. As I said, what they really wanted to know was, "How fast are GM, Ford, and Chrysler catching up to me?" And in talking to them, a couple of times people came right out with it: "The Detroit Three are never going to catch up with us. They don't have the mentality or the gumption." Now they're eating those words.

Every time I gave a speech on productivity, I used the example of my own family. I would tell everybody about my eight kids. They were all born in perfect order, boy-girl-boy-girl-boy-girl-boy-girl.

Everybody in the audience would say, "That's great productivity all right!"

And I'd say, "No, it's Vatican roulette!"

The meetings occasionally produced some unforgettable scenes. At Chrysler one year we drew a crowd of 40–50 people, including Bob Lutz, president, and Dick Dauch, the executive vice-president of manufacturing. Both are giant figures in Detroit. Lutz, a former Marine, is probably the best car guy in the business, but he also understands how auto companies operate. Recently he's been leading a design revival at GM. Dick Dauch, who played college football at Purdue, is a tough, oil-in-the-veins factory guy who retired from Chrysler to form American Axle, which bought and successfully operates a large chunk of GM's gear and axle manufacturing empire.

We got in there and started making our presentation. About one-third of the way through it, Dauch got up and started challenging our conclusions. Lutz told him, "Please, hold on. I want to hear the story." So we continued and in a few minutes Dauch was on his feet arguing again. He was getting mad; he didn't look too good. So Lutz calmed him down again. When we finished we asked for questions. Dauch jumped up and started tearing me apart. Well, I loved it. This was familiar ground to me. I've been to a hundred sessions in this conference room. Dauch was almost foaming at the mouth. Finally Lutz got up and said, "Shut the hell up! I've had enough of this! I want you to learn to listen." Well, Dauch kept going. Soon he and Lutz were practically toe-to-toe; and they're both huge people. I don't remember his exact words to Dauch, but Lutz finally said something like, "You don't want to mess with me. I was a Marine and I was trained to kill!"

Eventually, we began doing a *Harbour Report* for Europe. Over there, it's an entirely different animal. First of all, it isn't a public report. Secondly, it is run by engineers, and the auto companies that participate just want data, data, and more data. "Don't tell us how good or bad we are; we want to know why. What is the total number of welds in a car body, and what is the percentage done in-house? What percentage is done automatically, and what percentage is done manually?" The companies compare a range of manufacturing parameters like this, and anybody who is lagging gets the message. There's less concern in Europe about violating antitrust laws than in the U.S., where the Justice Department is always hovering in the background and any meeting among companies is usually attended by squads of antitrust lawyers. European automakers meet regularly to share internal data.

We found a way, however, to provide U.S. automakers with similar kinds of detailed comparative data about productivity and cost. American automakers are generally forbidden to share information about future products. But nothing prevents them from doing the same for existing products, except their own desire for confidentiality. This became an enormous business opportunity for us. Here's how it worked.

Auto Company X wanted to find out how it stacked up against the competition in the cost of making a certain product. We did engines, transmissions, even body-in-white, which is the industry's term for a completed car body before it goes to the paint shop. In some cases, we did entire cars. Company X would dump all its cost data on us, and we would go to all the other companies and get their similar data. When it was all compiled, we would call the companies back and make a presentation on what it cost Company A, B, C, D and X to make the product. Maybe it was a four-cylinder engine, or whatever. We never identified any of the companies by name, but sometimes it wasn't hard to figure out who was the winner. In fact, we never talked publicly about these studies at all, and the data is still locked away in safes. What the companies got out of it was a benchmark, or a cost target. What Harbour & Associates got out of it was expertise. Nobody knew as much about cost as we did.

A lot of things fell out of the comparative studies. For instance, in recent years I've been focused on trying to convince the U.S. automakers to standardize their use of thousands of commodity components. These are lower-cost items the automakers buy from outside suppliers, which usually don't define the vehicle's personality or performance, for example, things like fasteners, bearings, small electric motors, actuators, and even relatively complex systems like catalytic mufflers and air bags. Here was Honda with five catalysts, for instance. These are the devices in the exhaust system that remove pollutants. Honda had five for its entire product lineup worldwide. And there was Toyota with six. And here was GM with more than 100 catalysts. To make 100 catalysts required 200 dies to stamp out the metal tops and bottoms, which were loaded with a substrate that's coated with platinum, palladium, and rhodium and then welded together. GM, in sum, was taking a bath.

But the real drama we found in these annual studies was the improvement that GM, Ford, and Chrysler eventually achieved in quality and productivity.

In our first report in 1981, we said the Detroit firms easily needed 33–40 labor hours to assemble a vehicle, compared with an average of about 20 hours for the Japanese. On comparable small cars alone, the difference was 33 hours for the domestics and 17 for the Japanese. This meant that for every 1,000 small cars the domestic producers used 4,125 workers and the Japanese

2,125. To assemble a car and make its body stampings, engine, and automatic transmission, the Big Three required 60 labor hours or 7,500 workers. The Japanese needed just 3,850 workers. The first report also highlighted that Japanese manufacturers would average 550 major body panel stampings per hour, compared with 325 for the Detroit Three. Die change time from one body panel to the next was 5–6 minutes for the Japanese, and 4–6 hours for the domestics. This was generous; die changes in domestic plants often exceeded 8 hours and could skyrocket to 24 hours.

We also reported that unscheduled absences among workers at domestic plants were as high as 8 percent of the labor force and only 2.1 percent in Japan. This was not only a cost penalty. It had a major impact on quality, since every day the foreman in a domestic plant had to assign as many as 350 workers to fill in for those absent, often putting workers in jobs they weren't familiar with—so much for quality!

Now, take a look at the productivity improvement that's been made since then. Table 9-1 shows a more recent snapshot of the total average labor hours to assemble a car and truck. This includes all car models and all light duty trucks and sport utility vehicles (SUVs). Assembly hours for domestic producers in 1980 varied from 33 to 40; so, for the industry as a whole, this represents an improvement over 1980 of about 46 percent.

Table 9-1. Assembly hours per vehicle

Company	Car	Truck
Chrysler LLC	19.59	22.40
Ford	24.30	21.76
GM	20.97	23.13
Honda	20.19	23.34
Nissan	22.42	26.28
NUMMI	18.79	19.22
Toyota	20.24	27.85

Source: *Harbour Report* 2008

Another interesting way to look at this is to show how many assembly plants each automaker has on the top 10 list for productivity (Table 9-2). In 1980, not a single Big Three plant would have matched Japanese competitors in productivity.

Table 9-2. Number of car and truck assembly plants
on the top 10 list for productivity

Company	Cars	Trucks
Chrysler LLC	2	2
Ford	0	5
GM	4	2
NUMMI	1	1
Toyota	2	0
CAMI*	1	0

*CAMI is a joint venture between GM and Suzuki Motor Corp. in Ingersoll, Ontario.
Source: *Harbour Report* 2008

Metal stamping, of course, is a critical part of automobile manufacturing. I encourage readers to visit a full-scale automobile stamping plant if you ever get the chance, or to pay attention to the stamping lines that might be part of an assembly plant tour. The machinery is massive, wonderful. A major press line occupies as much space as a large two-story home and costs up to $50 million. Dies used to press steel sheets into the desired shape can weigh more than a Cadillac®. In operation, a die descends to the sheet metal with an authoritative thump, like a distant explosion. The ground trembles; if the plant wasn't built over bedrock or supported by a massive concrete substructure, it would quickly be shaken into pieces. In the old days, workers would stand between these ironclad monsters, grab a sheet out of one die and stick it into the next in line until the part was finished. Somebody at the end of the line then stacked the pieces for shipment. Today, a modern transfer press is highly automated; human hands don't touch the metal as the part passes from one station to another.

A typical vehicle body has more than 100 stamped steel pieces, and 15 to 20 of those are major panels. These include body sides, floor pans, doors, hoods, deck lids, and fenders. Historically, the automakers operated their own stamping plants to make the major panels, and they will continue to do so for the foreseeable future. Why not give the work to an outside supplier? Two reasons: the auto companies want absolute control of quality, and they also want to make a profit on body production rather than giving it to somebody else.

With the high capital expense involved in stamping, it's imperative that the press run at full speed. If the press is engineered for 15 strokes per minute, then the goal is 900 finished pieces per hour and 7,200 pieces per 8-hour shift, less whatever time is lost for worker relief, breakdowns and, very importantly, die changes. I've said several times that the Japanese changed dies in 5–10 minutes while the Big Three Detroit firms needed 4–6 hours in the 1980s. The domestics have focused for years on changing dies more quickly—in other words, you want to have that very expensive equipment making parts, not sitting idle. As a result, the American disadvantage has been sharply reduced. Current average times are shown in Table 9-3.

Table 9-3. Average time to complete die changes in major stamping presses making body panels

Company	Die Change Time (minutes)*
Toyota	7.8
Auto Alliance	11.4
NUMMI	12.7
CAMI	14.9
GM	19.6
Chrysler	25.6
Ford	27.9

*Average is based on all die changes for one year.
Source: *Harbour Report* 2008

The production of engines and automatic transmissions is largely an in-house business for all the automakers. Some have outsiders build manual transmissions because they're sold in relatively low volumes. There are also numerous joint ventures to build and supply powertrains. But in general, the auto companies want to control engine/transmission quality and technology. Of course, they're also reluctant to give the profit they make on powertrain production to outsiders.

Engines and transmissions are a major part of a vehicle's personality, and they also help define the automakers themselves. Honda, for instance, is probably best thought of as an engine maker. If you look at its whole product lineup—cars, motorcycles, marine engines, lawn mowers, power generators, and so forth—Honda makes about 30 million engines a year worldwide. Every Toyota engine has double overhead camshafts, a showy and expensive but highly marketable format that's financially possible because of the company's overall productivity. General Motors has decided to stick with high-tech overhead valve engines for its full-sized pickup trucks and SUVs; these are somewhat easier to make than the overhead camshaft type and offer proven durability.

Automotive engines today are far more complex than in 1980. To meet increasingly tough fuel economy and clean-air standards, automakers have replaced carburetors with fuel injection systems; sophisticated computer controls are in place everywhere; hundreds of internal changes have been made to reduce friction and boost efficiency; aluminum has replaced iron in blocks and heads; and innovations like variable valve timing, all but absent in 1980, are now common. Most 1980 cars used three-speed automatic transmissions. Today, six-speed gearboxes are common. The typical powertrain today has nearly twice as many manufactured parts as in 1980; but productivity has been improved dramatically, as shown in Table 9-4.

Compared to 1980, not to mention with my days in the forge plants at Chrysler, progress by firms in Detroit has been dramatic. How they did that is a complex story, with many failures as well as successes. The companies forced product engineering and

Table 9-4. Labor hours to produce engines and transmissions

Company	Engine	Automatic Transmission	Total Powertrain
Chrysler	3.35	3.36	6.71
Ford	4.32	3.62	7.94
General Motors	3.44	3.68	7.12
Toyota	3.13	3.17	6.30
Honda	3.53	NA	
Nissan	4.16	NA	
Average	3.66	3.58	7.24
Big Three average in 1980	6.80	6.60	13.40
2007 improvement over 1980	45%	46%	46%

Source: *Harbour Report* 2008

manufacturing to cooperate; they formulated detailed strategies to boost factory quality and productivity and pursued them religiously. Capital investments were massive—hundreds of billions of dollars were spent on new tools and equipment by the Detroit firms in the 1980s and 1990s—probably the biggest industrial spending plan in world history. They all fought for cultural changes as well, all the way from making top executive bonuses depend on quality to empowering workers at the assembly plant to stop the line if something went wrong. Belatedly, they saw the need to get back to using common systems, designs, and processes. They whipped suppliers for price concessions and boosted quality and delivery requirements. And the UAW contributed by, in general, not fighting productivity gains and showing some flexibility in work rules and job classifications. And they read the *Harbour Report*. This isn't the place to go into these changes in detail; you'd need 100 Harvard MBAs and thousands of pages to do that story justice. But it is worthwhile to take a closer look at one domestic company that, in my opinion, is getting well ahead of the game: General Motors.

Chapter 10

General Motors and the Three C's

"I remember very clearly at the first budget review having a pretty direct conversation with the head of manufacturing . . . We began to get huge improvements in productivity and responsiveness. I got a chance to see that firsthand."

"The big and the fast beat the small and the fast. If you check out the NBA today, they're big and fast."
—Rick Wagoner, CEO, General Motors Corp.

General Motors (GM) had to walk through the Valley of the Shadow of Death first, but now it's back on track. I mean, it has come back like an absolute animal. GM did that by rediscovering the Three C's of efficient manufacturing: *common, common,* and *common.* And what drove it back from unique to common was the *Harbour Report.* More specifically, what spurred GM was the comparative data from the *Harbour Report* in the hands of a determined leader. That guy is Rick Wagoner, now GM chairman and CEO, who gets my vote for auto industry executive of the decade.

In the early days of the report, we used to beat GM up regularly. The company was so far behind Honda and Toyota that it was ridiculous. Worse than that, I would personally beat up on Wagoner every time I saw him. In 1994 he was put in charge of North American operations, which was still strangling under the BOC-CPC reorganization of 1984. Nothing was getting done when he took over.

Everything was unique. Wagoner couldn't take a car out of BOC and put it in a CPC assembly plant. He couldn't take a stamping die out of a CPC press and put it in a BOC press or a Truck & Bus

Group press. Body architecture was different; they welded them differently in unique body shops. One body shop had a mechanical hemmer (a machine that puts a hem into inner and outer body panels so they can be joined) and another had a hydraulic or electrical hemmer. *Do me a favor: I want one type of hemmer so that it's in every plant and everybody knows how to run it.* I ached to call Wagoner up to tell him, but I knew I'd never get through. So I used to send him notes. "These are the things you should be addressing." And he would send back a note from time to time. Everything was unique, and the word he was getting from us was: *common.* He heard the same thing from his staff. He assigned them to tell him what the hell was going wrong, and they came back with, "We're all unique."

In 1994, Wagoner understood this, but he had just lost 10 years because of the 1984 reorganization. And, from his point of view, long product lead times in the auto industry meant it would take at least five years to untangle the mess and start putting in common manufacturing systems. In other words, go back to the way GM operated before 1984. Wagoner got approval from GM's North American Strategy Group, a top-level panel of executives, for a new reorganization.

I used to envy whoever it was that had GM's sign business. One day the sign in front of the building said Fisher Body Division. In a little while, it was changed to say BOC Group Headquarters, or whatever. Now all the signs in front of the plants were going to change again! To outsiders, it looked like GM had gone nuts. "What? Another reorganization—are they ever going to get it right?"

This time, Wagoner did get it right. Created this time were the General Motors Assembly Division in charge of all assembly plants; the Metal Fabricating Division in charge of all stamping plants; and the Powertrain Division in charge of engine and transmission plants. We should probably say they were re-created, because those organizations, in effect, were the ones that were ripped apart in 1984. Wagoner set up all kinds of metrics to guide these groups. They were targets for improvement in the basics of factory work. Measured were things like rates of repair and rework, first-time quality in the paint shop, first-time quality coming off the final assembly line, and so forth. Manufacturing people had to come in every quarter for a presentation on how they were measuring up with the plans. And Wagoner, believe me, took no prisoners. This is how the pursuit of the Three C's played out at GM:

- *common* body-shop facilities, tooling, and processing;
- *common* paint facilities and processing, particularly for new paint systems in assembly plants; and
- *common* assembly line facilities and tooling, but above all specific assembly line bills of process; in effect, every component and subassembly would be installed in the same workstation in every plant.

Plans were also drawn up to make assembly plants more flexible so that it was possible to build more than one platform in a single plant. This takes a long time to implement, since a basic vehicle platform design—generally speaking, the underbody that defines the car's length and width—normally is in production for at least 10 years.

My old nemeses, the product engineers, suffered a bit under the new strategy. For them, unique was golden. Traditionally, that's how they made their mark and got promoted—by coming up with a dramatic new design, usually something unique. They now had to adapt to being creative over a *common* underbody and architecture—something that didn't bother GM designers in the 1950s and 1960s. All future products would have *common* assembly processing—absolutely no exceptions.

Slowly, Wagoner's strategy took hold. Average labor hours to assemble a car dropped 25 percent from 1994 to 2003, while truck assembly hours were down 24 percent. Vehicle defects also were dropping substantially. "Commonizing" stamping plants was no easy task. Remember, in Japanese plants, every stamping press stood on the same footprint, and every die was made so it would fit in any press of the same size. At GM, the opposite was true. So, the company had to move as quickly as possible to change current press lines to common footprints, "commonizing" processes by part type and common die design and construction. In addition, stamping operations at GM had to put in just-in-time parts supply systems, establish common maintenance procedures and common quality systems, and perform faster die changes. By doing these things, GM got some impressive results in just three years. Here is a quote from a letter that Joe Spielman, general manager of the Metal Fabricating Division, wrote to employees in September, 1998:

> *"'I love it when a plan comes together.'" I'm referring to that famous one-liner used by George Peppard at the conclusion of each 'A-Team' TV adventure. It was very appropriate at Metal Fabricating Division (MFD) with the release of the 'Harbour Report' 1998. This data in this report will not only make the competition take notice, it should also be a source of professional pride for the men and women of MFD. Six of the top ten plants in transfer press hits per hour were GM. On average in that measure, GM blew by Ford, Chrysler, Honda, Nissan, and Toyota. In total hits per hour—with transfer, tandem, and major progressive combined—four of the top five plants, as reported by the 'Harbour Report,' were GM. Our investment in 'common' is paying off in equipment productivity, yet we have a lot of work to do in the area of pieces per worker. Our competition counted us out in the past, but no more . . . Four years ago we were a collection of plants and functions with different backgrounds, different cultures, different processes, different systems, and different equipment. Our main job—stamping metal—was about the only thing that was common across the division. Four years later, the picture has changed dramatically. MFD is a strong, unified division with an unwavering strategy based on 'common.'"*

The Powertrain Group also recorded impressive gains by implementing the Three C's: common, common, common. Engine manufacturing hours fell 39 percent from 1993 to 2003 while automatic transmission hours were cut 32 percent.

In 1998, Wagoner was named president and chief operating officer. He quickly went about implementing the same "common" ethic worldwide. It wasn't very long ago when GM would build a small car in the United States and a small car in Europe with substantially the same dimensions, design, and function, but without a single nut or bolt in common. Of course, the manufacturing and assembly systems were unique. Wagoner put in place worldwide targets for manufacturing productivity and quality, and appointed GM's first worldwide manufacturing executive to achieve them. Hand in hand with this, of course, was a product revival.

It became a cliché in the auto industry by the late 1980s that people would settle for a GM car, but that wasn't what they really wanted. In other words, there wasn't anything in the lineup that people lusted after. Now the company has numerous "aspirational" vehicles—just about everything in the Cadillac® lineup, the Buick Enclave®, the latest Chevrolet Malibu®, and others. One part of this revival is having product engineers who know what customers want; the bigger part, I'd have to say, is having a manufacturing system that can deliver quality and put a vehicle on the market with competitive features at a competitive cost.

GM's transformation is still a work in progress; the company's financial results show that the job obviously isn't done. But we can now see a time when the quality and productivity gap between GM and Toyota—so large and seemingly intractable when I first studied it in 1980—is no longer on the table.

Each year, the Detroit Auto Dealers Association sponsors a black-tie preview of the North American International Auto Show, with proceeds going to charity. It's Detroit's biggest annual social event, with just about every ranking auto executive in attendance. In January, 2005, my wife and I bumped into Wagoner at the Cadillac exhibit. After a handshake, I asked him if we could get together for a chat, no longer than one hour. "If you want one hour," he said, "that really means two hours." Demands on his time were heavy. Our meeting never took place and I completely understand why. The CEO of any auto company today doesn't need another hour added to his 12–14-hour daily schedule. So I'll tell him now what I planned to say then: *Congratulations on the 1994 decision to reorganize GM's North American operations to focus on 'common'; and on spending an enormous number of hours tracking each group's progress to improve quality and productivity; and finally, on the effort to spread the 'common' focus to all of GM's worldwide operations.*

Chapter 11

My days in Journalism, and the Everlasting Customer

"You had the courage to say some things that for some reason most reporters have been reluctant to get into."
—Lloyd Reuss, GM president,
in a letter to the author

"You've been the consummate pro in this business, and I'm personally grateful for the advice you have always been ready to provide over the years. I believe yours was the exact, direct, outspoken voice many of us needed at a critical time in our industry. We are all better for having listened."
—J. T. Battenberg III, chairman,
Delphi Automotive Systems,
in a letter to the author

I've spent my life telling people what they didn't want to hear. So it was natural at some point, I guess, that I would become a journalist. In October, 1985, I began to write a monthly column for *Automotive Industries* magazine, and this went on for 13 years. For the most part, I addressed these pieces to the "everlasting customer" who is, of course, the most important focus when you're running a factory or any other kind of business. I will quote from some of these here, because they sum up whatever there is in me of philosophy.

- "In Japan, manufacturing engineers are with a new product program from the start; in the U.S., product engineers think suggestions from manufacturing engineers amount to interference." (Harbour Nov. 1985)

- "Trying to inspect quality into a car, truck, transmission, or suspension after it has been built will never, absolutely never, improve quality. Sure, inspection is required; but in every workstation, not after the fact. So, you think it's easy to change to inspection in-station, right? Wrong! First, the union will scream when you try to eliminate thousands of inspectors and tell all the production workers they must do the job. (Remember, this is one of those work rules negotiated in good times to create more jobs.) Second, changing the present system means more than the elimination of separate inspectors, because once you start building quality in at each workstation, you'll end up getting rid of those repairmen needed to fix the defects in 20 to 25 percent of all the cars you build. Third, you can't just hand the production worker the job of inspection without some training." (Harbour Dec. 1985)

- "Every time I go into an American manufacturing plant, I hear the same complaint: 'We can't compete with the international competition because they have newer machinery.' But Japanese machinery is not newer. It just looks newer. The difference is that the Japanese use their machines, whereas we abuse them. In the U.S., we just don't maintain our equipment. In fact, we actually plan on having our stamping and machining plants go down 50 percent of the time they're supposed to be running." (Harbour Feb. 1986)

- "Why can't we approach a die change as if it were a pit stop in the Daytona 500? Four tires, a full tank, and you're back in the race in 15 seconds—or else. Could you imagine someone who wanted to win making a pit stop only to find the crew didn't have enough fuel, forgot to balance the tires, and left their tools back in the garage?" (Harbour May 1986)

- "It was shocking for me to analyze one of the industry's newest assembly plants (in the 1980s) to find out the plant was about 3 million square feet, produced about 860 cars per day, had 70 more robots than most comparable industry plants, and employed 4,300 hourly and salary workers.

Three million square feet (twice the size of its international competition), loaded with the latest technology equipment and producing a car in 37 to 38 total employee hours—that was exactly twice as many hours per car as any Japanese plant, new or old. Yet, the management at this plant continued to brag that it was one of the newest, most highly automated plants in the world. Believe me, the 'everlasting customer' could care less." (Harbour July 1986)

- ". . . So it's not hard to believe that another 400,000 (jobs) will be lost if the domestics lose another 4.7 million units (of production to the Japanese). Clean up your act, company management and UAW management or this once dynamic industry will be but a skeleton of what it once was. Take no consolation in believing these 400,000 potential job losses will be covered by pensions, because the lowest hourly and salary workers on the seniority totem pole will go. The real point is: Don't leave as your legacy a non-competitive industry where your children have no opportunity to get a job." (Harbour Dec. 1986)

- "In the past when Lee Iacocca would go on TV and say, 'If you can find a better car, buy it,' that generally meant you had to drive to the next dealer. But recently Chrysler's product quality has actually achieved what Lee has been bragging about for years." (Harbour Apr. 1987)

- "The answer (to how Detroit should conduct strategic planning) is not so simple. In fact, it's quite complex. But when you get down to it, most companies first define their strategic goals in financial terms, based on their financial resources. As a result, our strategic planning process is seriously flawed. Why? Because it flows in the wrong direction. Executives are handed the financial goals, then they go off and develop individual actions of their own to support the overall plan . But in the process, many important questions are never answered." (Harbour May 1987)

- "What we find when we analyze the best manufacturers in the world (and, by the way, they're not only in Japan) is that every one has a philosophy, a mission. This philosophy is the foundation on which all operations and decisions of the company are ultimately based. Yet, a philosophy is only the foundation successful companies build on, because below that structure is a well-conceived and defined product system." (Harbour Oct. 1987)

- "Most (domestic) component plants have a very detailed plan—unfortunately, it's often a plan to go out of business." (Harbour Nov. 1987)

- "Funny, everyone seems to be learning that if you can't measure and chart it, you can't improve it." (Harbour Jan. 1988)

- "The next time I hear the term 'world class' uttered by any executive, the following response will be easy—'define it or shut up.'" (Harbour Sept. 1988)

- "One of the hottest topics in the industry today is product development time. And with the Japanese as the recognized leaders in this area, the U.S. automakers are working hard to reduce their lead times from five to six years to something less than four years. Unfortunately, with all the focus on the time required to develop a new model, a more important factor has been overlooked. And that is the money required to design, engineer, and tool a new vehicle. Reducing product development time and renewing vehicles more frequently is a smart strategy. But if you can't afford the capital expense, then what's the point?" (Harbour Dec. 1991)

- "No, we'd better not be willing to surrender our automotive industry or industrial base to Japan or any other country. True, this industry has its problems—a government without an industrial policy, a union immersed in politics, a healthcare industry that is out of control, high capital costs, and a stupid trade policy. But the American public better understand that one out of every seven workers in this country owes his job directly or indirectly to this industry. If there is no domestic auto industry, what will happen to the 'everlasting customer?'" (Harbour Apr. 1992)

- "The Japanese have one key trait that pervades all levels of their organizations—an obsession with reducing cost. Whether it's using the backside of a piece of paper, turning down the heat, or using a better tool to optimize steel utilization, the mentality is—'how can I reduce the cost in every area of the business?' Historically, domestic manufacturers have designed a vehicle and fully determined its features and content up front, leaving it to engineering and manufacturing to worry about cost. Typically, costs overrun the price the market will bear, requiring rebates and rollbacks. The bottom line is that everyone in the organization must be cost-conscious. It's an attitude we can't leave at home." (Harbour May 1992)

- "Resisting the temptation to cut manpower first to achieve cost reductions is difficult. But cutting manpower to force improvement doesn't always work—product output may decrease, overtime will increase, and quality problems will go up. Finding a way to use people in a team effort to identify and implement sustainable cost reduction ideas can work. But it has to be done before the plant gets into deep trouble." (Harbour July 1992)

- "Like winning the lottery, Americans always want to get rich quick, or in this case 'leapfrog' the competition. GM and other companies thought they could spend their way out of their quality and productivity problems; many failed miserably. As has been said before, long-term, sustainable improvements will only come from thousands of small incremental improvements." (Harbour Sept. 1992)

- "Ultimately, the biggest benefit from a huge gas tax increase would be forcing the domestic automakers to design, develop, and engineer much more fuel-efficient vehicles. Regardless of how unpopular an added gas tax would be, the long-term benefit could be a lower budget deficit, better roads, more fuel-efficient cars, less waste of natural resources, cleaner air, and more economic stability for the 'everlasting customer.'" (Harbour March 1993)

REFERENCES

Harbour, James E. 1985. "Product Engineering: The 'Buck' Starts Here." *Automotive Industries*, November.

—. 1985. "Why You Can't Inspect in Quality." *Automotive Industries*, December.

—. 1986. "Maintaining the Competitive Edge." *Automotive Industries*, February.

—. 1986. "Build Beautiful Bodies in Five Easy Steps." *Automotive Industries*, May.

—. 1986. "Is New-Tech Really the Answer?" *Automotive Industries*, July.

—. 1986. "Unemployment: The Price of Overcapacity." *Automotive Industries*, December.

—. 1987. "Building Quality the Chrysler Way." *Automotive Industries*, April.

—. 1987. "New Strategies for Strategic Planning." *Automotive Industries*, May.

—. 1987. "Understanding Your Competition." *Automotive Industries*, October.

—. 1987. "Can Component Plants Compete?" *Automotive Industries*, November.

—. 1988. "Get Control of Your Processes!" *Automotive Industries*, January.

—. 1988. "Choking." *Automotive Industries*, September.

—. 1991. "Time and Money." *Automotive Industries*, December.

—. 1992. "Get Rid of the Industry?!" *Automotive Industries*, April.

—. 1992. "Money as a Drug." *Automotive Industries*, May.

—. 1992. "Cutting Manpower too Quickly." *Automotive Industries*, July.

—. 1992. "Juicy Rationalizations." *Automotive Industries*, September.

—. 1993. "Back to the Future." *Automotive Industries*, March.

Chapter 12

Why It Hasn't Worked

"We've been a very nuts-and-bolts and transaction-oriented industry. We've viewed customers as always telling us about our problems. We never thought about the customers' costs after the sales—insurance, resale value, recycling. We've been too engineering and manufacturing focused."
—Jacques Nasser, before he was fired
as Ford Motor Co. CEO in October, 2001

In 2000, I retired from Harbour & Associates. Ken had left the company, and I turned it over to Ron and Laurie. But I haven't stopped studying the auto industry. Every day I devour every bit of information that I can. Walking the factory floor is still my favorite thing, and I get to do that frequently in regular consulting jobs that I take on, mostly for smaller-to-medium-sized manufacturers who are fighting some problem or other.

I heard former Notre Dame football coach Lou Holtz talking about retirement. He said, "They ask me all the time. When the hell are you going to retire?" He replies, "I'm never retiring. You've got to understand something. When you retire you don't get days off anymore." That's where I am right now.

A lot of my time, however, has been taken up with probing a mystery: General Motors, Ford, and Chrysler have made impressive gains against the Japanese in quality and manufacturing efficiency. So why are they still getting their butts kicked by Honda and Toyota? They remain dangerously uncompetitive in profit performance and continue to lose market share. Laurie and I have spent months looking for an answer, and here it is: *they simply haven't completed their transition to a Toyota-style business model*. The Detroit Three are still fighting a range of structural problems that relate mostly to their historical, cultural, and contractual differences from the Japanese. We found that, for the most part, efforts are under way to address them. But in many cases the solutions Detroit automakers are implementing haven't yet become routine, disciplined, and universally understood aspects of their business practices and corporate cultures.

Time is running short. Unless Detroit takes decisive action, the gap could grow. Kaizen, or continuous improvement, remains a driving force for the Japanese automakers. Toyota, for instance, wrung $1,000 per vehicle out of its cost of North American and worldwide production simply in the initial phase of an all-out effort to increase the number of standard commodity components across its vehicle lineup. Credibly, Japan's No. 1 automaker has set a goal of reducing major non-commodity component costs by 30 percent.

In 2007, Toyota enjoyed a $1,651 profit-per-vehicle advantage over GM in North America, $2,389 over Ford, and $1,334 over Chrysler. This gives the No. 1 Japanese automaker a decisive edge in configuring, equipping, and marketing its vehicles. Nissan and Honda also enjoy large advantages over GM, Ford, and Chrysler. Some of this is due to labor issues. The UAW, I believe, has gone along with Detroit's productivity drive. But I'll bet there isn't a single plant manager in a GM, Ford, or Chrysler factory in the U.S. who wouldn't rather boot the union out the door. The companies and their unions still must solve the following problems.

- *Absenteeism* has always been a major issue. It directly affects quality when a number of workers are assigned to a new job every day to replace people who called in sick.

- *Restrictive work rules* literally define what each worker can and cannot do. In most cases, there's no technical, operational, or humane justification for these rules, and they simply raise production costs.

- *Heavy penalties for healthcare* for both active and retired workers are crippling. The recent contract negotiated by the Detroit companies and the UAW shifts responsibility for retiree healthcare to the UAW, potentially relieving Detroit of a crushing burden that the Japanese companies don't have. But the new system will cost billions of dollars in badly needed cash, and it doesn't take effect until 2010, and every day it's more problematic whether Detroit can wait that long.

- *Jobs bank programs* are a longstanding feature of UAW contracts, which keep workers on the payroll after they have lost their jobs permanently. For the three companies overall, this is a multi-billion-dollar program. Of course, the Japanese have nothing like this.

- *Supplemental unemployment benefits* (SUB) are paid by the Detroit firms to workers who are laid off temporarily. These are designed to combine with state unemployment benefits to maintain idled workers at more than 90 percent of regular pay while they're off the job. These impose another substantial cost penalty and force the automakers to consider keeping factories in operation above levels of market demand, boosting the need for price incentives.

But labor contracts only represent about 10–20 percent of the problem. We found many other issues that the Detroit companies must address before they can become profitable, viable competitors. It's a complex story, just as you would expect when you're making a product with about 15,000 separate parts. But I think it's important for America to understand them, so here they are in detail.

1. Each of the manufacturers must "commonize" their worldwide passenger car and truck platforms to greatly reduce investment for design and product development, new body shops, assembly lines, stamping tools and dies, and supplier tooling. A look at Ford can highlight the problem and the potential. Ford has four unique Fiesta® platforms and three unique Focus® platforms worldwide. These seven platforms drive separate worldwide product design and engineering efforts and investment. There are too many unique and

costly components, unique body shops and vehicle assembly lines, and unique tools and dies, resulting in out-of-control investment costs. The future new Fiesta car will have one worldwide common platform as will the Focus. The potential cost savings will be monumental since there will be common chassis, powertrain and body components, common body shops, common assembly lines, and only one design and engineering staff for each platform.

2. All these new platforms must be engineered using common body architectures. This will allow select assembly plants to be totally flexible. That is, they'll be able to switch production from one model to another as the market dictates, but quickly and without additional investment. Honda is a good model for that today. Any unibody platform/model can be assembled in any plant, so that one production line can be used to build, for example, both the Civic® and Accord®. Common body architecture means separate platforms are designed so that they are welded and assembled using the same facilities, tools, and processes. General Motors has focused on common body architecture for all its new body platforms. Jim Queen, GM vice president of worldwide product engineering, now has the assignment to incorporate "common" around the world. Even better, he has the authority to enforce it.

The best application of the "common" approach is in the manufacture of vehicle bodies involving huge investments for stamping dies and presses, and welding equipment. The U.S. tool and die industry until recently was made up of hundreds of small- and mid-size tool shops that designed, built, and tested dies before they went to the stamping plant. The Big Three automakers also designed and built their own tools and dies. Typically, GM made 50 percent of the dies it needed to make a body, Ford 30 percent, and Chrysler 20 percent. Unfortunately, die design and construction by the outside tool shops and in-house designers were all unique. There was no such thing as a common die design, which is so basic to the Japanese cost advantage. In other words, you couldn't use a die designed and built for press line A in press line B. So, the cost of dies was out of sight.

A typical set of four hood dies could cost $1.8 to $2.2 million and the cost for all the body stampings for one new car could exceed $60 million. The Japanese took a totally different approach. They set precise standards for tool and die design and construction, for doors, body sides, deck lids, fenders, hoods, quarter panels, and floor pans. Every die had to be exactly the same except for the sculptured surface. Dies from different platforms or models could all be loaded in the same size presses in any stamping plant.

One of the main goals in the 1994 General Motors reorganization was to convert the company's entire body stamping group to common die designs and construction, common stamping press lines, and common parts processing. GM blitzed its in-house tool shops and outside suppliers by setting common standards for die design and construction of major parts such as doors or hoods. Further, the company set exacting specifications for all in-house press-line facilities, including die change and automation equipment. The result: total flexibility, greater quality and productivity, and a 40–50 percent reduction in stamping die costs. These gains haven't been without pain. As GM became more efficient, it decided to build all of its major dies in-house. In southeast Michigan, if you drove down just about any industrial lane, you'd pass some prosperous tool and die shops. Today, most of them are out of business. Much the same has happened at Chrysler, where Warren Miller, vice president of stamping (he's the guy who went from GM to Honda and then to Chrysler) has totally "commonized" its tool and die design and construction.

3. Common platforms and architecture will dictate the use of common commodity components. These include things like seat tracks, horns, lumbar supports, sensors, bearings, lock sets, door handles, and various hardware and fasteners.

In the past, unique platforms required unique components, which meant way too much was being spent for design and product engineering and tooling. One of the domestic manufacturers, for example, used more than 70 distinctly designed horns, while a Japanese competitor needed only two of them to equip all of its vehicles. Something is definitely wrong when you're paying through the nose for horns!

Commodity parts generally are low in cost, but an all-out effort to rationalize their use can tune up the bottom line as you wouldn't believe. Toyota has saved $1,000 per vehicle or $9.0 billion annually by "commonizing" 170 commodity components. The Detroit automakers have been working this side of the business, but for the most part they've only made major gains when each platform is redesigned. That could take 10 years or more! Why wait? Many of these components, like horns, could and should not wait for a complete vehicle redesign to be made common. A focused effort could accelerate this process.

4. The automakers must "commonize" non-commodity components. The potential is staggering, possibly saving another $1,000 per vehicle when you evaluate what Toyota and Honda have accomplished. These include major, high-value, design- and manufacturing-intensive components such as fuel systems, electrical systems, steering, brakes, engines, traction controls, suspensions, catalytic converters, heating and air conditioning, electronic and computer controls, some body stampings, and seat frames. Take a look at mirrors. One domestic automaker has 81 side-view mirrors for only one vehicle model while its principle competitor has only two. Another company has 40 separate front seat frames compared to only five at a major competitor. Just imagine the design and product engineering effort and cost being wasted, not to mention the production complexity imposed on the mirror and seat manufacturers.

One domestic manufacturer had engineered over 100 separate catalytic converters for its car and truck products. It did so because it thought a unique design for different vehicles would cut the use of the costly exotic materials used in these devices: platinum, palladium, and rhodium. But these multiple catalysts required that over 200 different top and bottom stampings be tooled. The plant making these catalysts had the monumental task of handling over 200 die changes to make all the stamped parts. How do you run a lean shop under those circumstances? It's impossible. This company's Japanese competitors had only five or six converters for their entire product lineup because they evaluated the total system cost, not just the exotic materials' cost.

Once again, the Big Three are trapped by their history. For the most part, they don't have a disciplined system where a group executive looks across all vehicle platforms to maximize the use of common components. But that too is beginning to change.

The combination of new common body platforms, common body architecture, and common commodity and non-commodity components has the potential to save, conservatively, $2,000 per vehicle and reduce investment costs by 40 percent. But the impact of this drive will fall most immediately and heavily on the industry's beleaguered suppliers of parts, components, and systems. Suppliers already have suffered far more extensively than the big auto manufacturers. Many have been forced into bankruptcy because of lower production volumes, severe price cuts, rising material costs, their own inefficiency, and uncompetitive labor contracts. Delphi Corp., Collins & Aikman Corp., Tower Automotive, and Dana Corp. are examples of once-strong companies that were forced to reorganize under Chapter 11 of the U.S. Bankruptcy Code or liquidate because of the unforgiving competitive environment.

Pressure on all suppliers is huge and likely will grow. Especially vulnerable are the smaller, privately held suppliers that offer parts and services to the larger suppliers. The in-house restructuring we believe is necessary to restore

Detroit to full health could take years, while suppliers will be forced to live with bulls-eyes on their backsides, the targets of continual price cut demands from the Big Three.

5. Currently, very few U.S. assembly plants can assemble more than one vehicle platform in the same body shop on the same assembly line, a critical requirement in today's highly segmented auto market. When the rising price of gasoline sent customers in search of small, fuel-efficient cars in 2008, the Japanese had an advantage because they could more quickly boost production of those vehicles. The Detroit firms pay heavily for this lack of flexibility with excess capacity and higher capital investment per vehicle than their Japanese counterparts.

6. The Big Three automakers have substantially reduced their excess capacity in a painful, decades-long series of plant closures. But in the market downturn in 2008, additional assembly lines went quiet. Table 12-1 compares capacity utilization at the Detroit Three with their Japanese rivals.

In 2008, factory output has dropped to levels not seen since the 1990s. Plant utilization—remember, idle plants are losing money—likely will dive from 88 percent to around 70 percent, multiplying losses. Further, there will be the

Table 12-1. Assembly plant utilization in 2007

Company	Capacity Utilization	Assembly Lines	Excess Units
Toyota	100%	8	—
Honda	97%	7	50,000
General Motors	88%	26	520,000
Chrysler LLC	88%	13	350,000
Ford Motor Co.	84%	17	520,000
Nissan Motor	80%	5	290,000

Source: *Harbour Report* 2008

added negotiated costs for job security payments to laid-off workers. Each manufacturer faces a critical decision: How much more capacity should be shut down? The answer fully depends on the following:

- Will the light-duty truck market rebound and how much?
- Will there be a permanent market shift to small/mid-size cars?
- Will the Japanese continue to capture more market share and build more new capacity?
- Will the new federal rules on fuel economy result in more import cars from the Far East?
- How fast can the Big Three automakers design, engineer, and bring to production new fuel-efficient products?

GM, Ford, and Chrysler once rode out market downturns like battleships in a gale. But today they're considerably weaker financially—in the middle of an historic and dramatic downturn in the U.S. economy and the new vehicle market. Even before the crash they were recording huge losses on auto operations, and their cash reserves may only be enough to carry them through 2009. The enormous cost to design, engineer, and build products to meet the new fuel-economy standards probably cannot be capitalized from projected production/sales volumes and cash flow.

7. Chrysler, Ford, and General Motors have practically eliminated the once-gaping productivity and quality gap with their Japanese rivals, according to the 2008 surveys by J. D. Power & Associates and Harbour & Associates. Nevertheless, car-for-car and truck-for-truck, the Detroit companies are losing money and the Japanese are profitable. The main difference is revenue per vehicle: the Detroit companies still realize fewer dollars per vehicle sold because they remain on the treadmill of high sales incentives and rock-bottom pricing for vehicles sold to rental car fleets. In particular,

Toyota and Honda have been able to command higher prices, in part because of the perception that they offer better quality and value. However justified that perception was in the past, it doesn't apply to most of Detroit's latest offerings. While the Japanese wait for America to catch up with the fact that a Chevrolet Malibu® is just as good as a Honda Accord®, the Detroit Three are forced to make another tough calculation that their Japanese rivals don't face: How to balance the cost of price incentives against the cost of job security provisions in UAW contracts. When production is cut, Detroit companies must continue to pay idle workers, while the Japanese have no comparable handicap. Every day the Detroit companies have to decide where to take the hit: by cutting prices to customers and, hopefully, keeping the production line going, or by paying workers not to work.

When we looked at sales incentives for September 2008, a month of huge sales declines, we weren't surprised to find that Chrysler's average sales incentives were $4,705 per vehicle. GM was at $3,972 and Ford at $3,696. That compared with Honda's $1,047, Toyota's $1,481, and Nissan's $2,376. In effect, the Detroit Three were putting an average of $2,300 more on the hood of every vehicle sold. September was a horrible month industry-wide for sales, but the average $2,300 gap was similar throughout 2008.

Further, to boost factory output, the Detroit firms for years have depended on heavily discounted sales to vehicle fleets, especially to car rental agencies, to keep factories running as near as possible to output. Many fleet sales are profitable, but not those that go to the car rental companies. Price cuts to rental agencies range between $3,500 and $4,500 per vehicle, a heavy drain on revenue for the Detroit Three. In the near past, fleet sales accounted for as much as 25 percent of U.S. sales volume among the Big Three. But there's no market for the Detroit companies, or the Japanese either, for that matter, if they simply raise prices. Worse, the search for optimum market value, as the "everlasting customer" sees it, will be more complicated in the future.

All automakers are scrambling to bring new fuel-efficient cars and trucks to market. That process will not occur overnight. The future is clouded because of new federal mandates for enhanced fuel efficiency and reductions in tailpipe emissions. It has been said, and I believe it's true, that a typical 2008 model car puts out less air pollution going down the freeway at 75 miles per hour than a typical 1968 car did while sitting in the driveway with the engine turned off. (That's because the older model had no controls over evaporating fumes from the fuel system and crankcase.) The car companies don't yet know how they will meet the new regulations, but they have one word to describe all of them: *costly*. The North American car market has been strong over the past 15 years because sticker price hasn't really been an issue. But 10 years from now, we could see the return of sticker shock with a vengeance. Europe is your model: just look at the average small car price there in comparison to a similar vehicle in America.

So, Laurie and I found that with all the catching up Detroit has done, it still is a long way from the mountaintop. And even when it gets to that summit, there's another entire area where Detroit has been stomped down: the terms of international trade.

Chapter 13

A Word About Trade

"Washington, Aug. 13, 1968 (AP)—The U.S. and Japan are near agreement to liberalize the imports of American automobile parts and permit large investments by U.S. automakers in Japan. But final accord has eluded the negotiators."

"President Bush missed a huge opportunity to negotiate a meaningful reduction in our trade deficit with Japan . . . He sat down and bargained with Japan and they gave him the sleeves off their vest."
—Owen Bieber, UAW president,
February 1992

Most people have forgotten it, but Detroit is the home of free trade. It's too bad that we can't say the same about places like Tokyo, Seoul, Beijing, and Berlin. Part of the pain felt today by U.S. automakers comes from trade policies designed to give foreigners a piece of our pie, while we didn't demand a piece of theirs. For Americans, trade policy is part of politics. We give some of our wealth to countries so that they won't go communist or fundamentalist or join any other enemies of democracy. Nobody else looks at it the same way. For the rest of the world trade is purely business, and foreign governments dole out help to their own industries, not to others.

Look at the worldwide trade in oil. If you take politics out of the equation, there's no good reason why our heavy dependence on imports of foreign oil should be viewed as such an awful thing. If it were a simple business transaction, oil from Tehran would be just as good for us as oil from Texas. For Europe and Japan, being heavily import-dependent works well. This is because they don't play politics. It used to be a standard joke: "We're 100 percent dependent on Scotland for imports of Scotch whiskey, and nobody complains about that." We used to raise these issues regularly in Washington, and were told to quit whining. Life, indeed, is not fair.

Free trade is a strong drug that most people don't like to swallow. It's like chemotherapy—it might help you if it doesn't kill you. The benefit of free trade is generally years in the future, while the pain is immediate. People lose their jobs and get pushed into poverty waiting for the beneficial future to arrive. Just take a look at Detroit, Flint, Saginaw, Toledo, Akron, Cleveland, and dozens more American towns. It's no wonder that free trade is rarely practiced in the world. What could be more unpopular? In Detroit we know this better than anyone else does because the standard pattern of the modern free-trade agreement was set right here. That came in 1965 with the U.S.-Canada Auto Pact. This agreement certainly changed the way we did business at Chrysler Corp., and it was the same for General Motors Corp. and Ford Motor Co.

I used to believe that Europe had high taxes on gasoline and astronomical taxes on big automobile engines because countries there wanted to encourage fuel conservation. Perhaps that's the practical impact of those regulations today. If so, we've evolved into that situation, because the original intent, I discovered while reading Ford's history, was to keep American cars out of the European market. It was sheer protectionism.

Ford Motor Co. began an international expansion drive in its earliest days. This was not long after it had completed its massive Rouge Industrial Complex southwest of Detroit—the biggest in the world circa 1919. It built a similar factory at Dagenham, England, and threatened to make the Model T as popular in Europe as in the United States. European automakers couldn't match Ford's efficiency, so they convinced home governments to slap a protective tax on the Model T engine, which was bigger in displacement than the run-of-the-mill, European-built car. Ford and GM were forced to work within those restrictions. Ford of

Europe and GM's Opel and Vauxhall brands eventually became fully integrated producers in Europe, which meant the vehicles they built there had exactly the same local content and local economic contribution as Volkswagen, Fiat, Renault, Jaguar, Mercedes, and the rest. There were no massive exports from the U.S. Meanwhile, the Europeans were free to ship whatever they wanted to America.

After World War II, with the Soviets on the threshold, the U.S. decided to rebuild Western Europe. So the U.S. opened the door to motor vehicle imports. Volkswagen (VW) did the best job among the European automakers, flooding America with the German-built Beetle® and small vans. That continued until VW became a casualty of the 1963 Chicken War.

How the Chicken War unfolded is interesting because it shows the adverse effects of government intervention in trade policy. The war started in 1962, when the European economic community raised tariffs on American chickens. The U.S. poultry industry was like Ford with the Model T. It had gotten to be so efficient that it could raise a chicken in America, ship it to Europe, and put it on sale in a German market at a significantly lower price than the German chicken farm a few miles away. Free trade and farming don't mix. Governments generally do whatever they can to protect their farmers, and America is just as bad. Anyway, there was a diplomatic exchange regarding the chicken tariffs with no good result for the Americans, who retaliated by slapping a tariff of 25 percent on imported trucks. In 1963, Volkswagen's bus—classified as a truck for tariff purposes—was extremely popular. It still is today, if you can find one in good shape. But the tariff pretty much wiped that business out, and the VW brand in America began a long, steady decline. Detroit automakers hadn't asked for the tariff. They thought they could meet Volkswagen's threat with their own small passenger vans, just as they had offered small cars to counter the Beetle.

The Chicken War tariff did have some positive consequences for America, but they were unforeseen and unintended. Toyota later discovered that its small Japan-built pickup trucks would qualify for a lower tariff if shipped to the U.S. without the cargo box. In that condition, they could be classified as parts, not vehicles. So Toyota opened its first plant in the U.S.—a factory to make cargo boxes in Long Beach, California. Nissan went a step further, opting to assemble its small pickup at its first U.S. plant in Smyrna, Tennessee.

U.S. automakers also found themselves blocked in Asia. Japan kicked them out in the 1930s, and they've never found their way back. In the years immediately following World War II, there was a danger that communists would grab control of the Japanese government. They were visibly trying to do that. So we gave the Japanese auto industry free access to the rich American market, and for decades—up to the present day, in fact—tolerated the tariffs, regulations, and subterfuges that kept their market closed to American products. You can argue that GM, Ford, and Chrysler never tried very hard to sell cars in Japan, but perhaps they would have done better if they hadn't been deliberately excluded.

At one point in the mid-1980s there was a big controversy about whether Japanese automakers were pricing their exports to minimize U.S. corporate income-tax payments. I distinctly remember that Chrysler Chairman Lee A. Iacocca claimed one year that he had personally paid more to the IRS than the entire Japanese auto industry! Iacocca hadn't much cause for complaint; he had gotten rich off of Chrysler stock options after the company came roaring back from the bailout days. Iacocca was famous for hyperbole, but the claim does show how goofy things can get when the terms of trade are all in one party's favor.

Detroit showed its true colors on trade in the 1965 U.S.-Canada Auto Pact. Up to that point, Canada's auto industry was dominated by the Detroit companies. Relatively high tariffs hobbled the direct export of cars and trucks to Canada from the United States. GM, Ford, and Chrysler assembled vehicles in Canada, but in plants that were no match for their American counterparts in productivity. Car prices in Canada were high, and the market was too small to justify the kind of high-volume plants that pumped out cars at a rate of 60 per hour in the United States. But Canada was a wealthy country with market growth potential for cars and trucks. The Big Three were eager to tap that potential. So the governments of the two nations hammered out a deal that, in essence, served as a pattern for all the U.S. free-trade agreements that followed: NAFTA, CAFTA, Australia, Bahrain, Chile, Israel, Jordan, Morocco, Singapore, and more.

Canada agreed to drop its tariffs on imports of U.S.-built cars and trucks, providing that the Detroit-based automakers manufacture vehicles and vehicle parts in Canada of a value to match their Canadian sales. To do this, the Detroit automakers had to invest heavily in assembly and parts manufacturing plants in Canada. Essentially, the border was gone. A GM assembly plant in Canada had to be just as efficient as one in Indiana; a Ford engine plant in Ontario would supply numerous assembly plants in the United States.

There were some objections to the arrangement. The UAW complained that Canada would get more factory jobs out of the deal than America, which was perfectly true. Canada was getting what the UAW would later fight for unsuccessfully: a local content law specifying that every Big Three car or truck sold in Canada must have a specified level (about 60 percent, although the calculation was complicated) of Canadian value-added content. The deal worked. Canada's car market grew, along with its economy overall.

The same was repeated in the mid-1990s in Mexico under the North American Free Trade Agreement (NAFTA). Mexico dropped restrictions on sales of foreign cars in exchange for so-called rules of origin requiring higher levels of Mexican content in new cars and trucks. The promise for Mexico was the same: full integration in an efficient North American automotive market. Ever since, the market there has been on a sharp growth path. In fact, in the first eight months of 2008, Mexico assembled 1,202,797 new cars and trucks, closing in on Canada's total of 1,270,623 for the same period, according to the trade publication, *Ward's Automotive Reports*.

Japan was following a different course. Industrial policy was set by the powerful Ministry of International Trade and Industry, the legendary MITI. This agency had decreed that Japan would be an export-oriented economy, and it used the full range of government powers—notably taxation, tariffs, customs procedures, and currency exchange values—to ensure that more vehicles left Japan than entered there. Later, Korea and China would follow the same pattern.

There was no U.S. local content requirement except in one instance. When Congress was drawing up the first Corporate Average Fuel Economy (CAFÉ) law in the 1970s, the UAW had won approval for a 75 percent North American content requirement for all vehicles used to calculate the fuel economy performance of Big Three domestic car fleets. Anything less than that would be counted as an import and would be calculated separately. This was simply aimed at preventing the Big Three from importing small cars to meet CAFÉ standards instead of building them here. It's doubtful that requirement saved a single American job. By and large, employment growth, as a result of Japan's growing market share in the U.S., has gone to Japan. Germany, France, and Italy also had industrial policies specifically favoring growth in their auto industries.

In America, industrial policy has always been a dirty word. The U.S. Department of Commerce and the U.S. International Trade Commission have formal departments or offices specifically aimed at fostering American manufacturing and watching out for injurious trade policies by our partners around the world. But mostly what those bureaucrats do is record the damage rather than take a direct hand in helping Detroit automakers compete.

In 2007, the Detroit automakers sold 14,338 U.S.-built vehicles in Japan. In that year, Japanese automakers sold 2,176,958 Japan-built vehicles in the U.S. Sales of American cars and trucks in Korea in 2007 were similarly negligible, versus sales of 523,594 Hyundai and Kia vehicles in America in the first eight months of 2008. You can just imagine what will happen when China gets its automobile export machinery cranked up.

If I had a choice between quality and productivity on one hand, and favorable government trade policy on the other, I'd have to go with the former—but with reservations. Hot competition in North America has made GM, Ford, and Chrysler substantially the equals of Toyota and Honda in quality and factory productivity, if not quite yet in total cost.

Nevertheless, American trade policy, consciously allowing others to take advantage of us, has created some doubt as to whether quality and productivity are enough. This is what the Detroit automakers really mean when they talk about fair versus free trade, or when they complain about Japan, China, and Korea rigging the exchange values of their currencies. Trade policy has been active in the automotive world for nearly a century, with Detroit consistently getting screwed. Maybe Iacocca said it best when Chrysler was going for a $1.2 billion bailout in 1979: "The government bailed us into this mess, so they should rightfully bail us out." In 2008, this debate is back with a $25 billion vengeance.

Chapter 14

Whither the Big Three?

"To anyone who would listen, I continually stressed that Chrysler wasn't an isolated case. Instead, we were a microcosm of what was going wrong in America and a kind of test lab for everybody else. No industry in the world got hit harder than autos. Government regulation, the energy crisis, and the recession were almost enough to put us away."

"Loan guarantees, I soon learned, were as American as apple pie."
—Lee A. Iacocca in
"Iacocca, An Autobiography"

When this chapter was written, two "B" words were being whispered in Detroit: bailout and bankruptcy. The situation was very similar to 1979, when Lee A. Iacocca went on his ultimately successful quest for government loan guarantees to rescue the failing Chrysler Corp. But there are major differences. The biggest, obviously, is the scale of destruction in Detroit, and the proposed solution. Chrysler went to the government alone back then. It asked for $1.5 billion in loan guarantees, and ended up withdrawing $1.2 billion. Ford also was in serious trouble, but managed to draw cash out of its highly profitable European arm to rescue its troubled U.S. unit. GM, in 1979, had begun its downward spiral but was still sitting on tons of cash. It was able to sit back and scoff at Chrysler's bailout play, mainly because top GM executives at that time didn't realize how close the No. 1 automaker was to its own reckoning. I'll never forget GM Chairman Tom Murphy telling a reporter that he didn't think the government should prop up failing companies. When asked about that quote at a news conference, UAW President Doug Fraser replied: "Tom Murphy is a horse's ass."

In 2008, GM and Ford shed their pride and joined Chrysler in asking Uncle Sam to cosign a loan. The Detroit Three at first sought $50 billion in federally guaranteed loans. That, GM said, was only half of what it will cost the U.S. auto industry to meet new Corporate Average Fuel Economy (CAFÉ) standards that begin to take effect in 2011. But they were lucky to get Congressional and White House approval for half that amount.

Here is another similarity between 1979 and 2008: America was going through a third oil shock in the summer of 2008, and people were abandoning the big pickup trucks and sport utility vehicles (SUVs) from GM, Ford, Chrysler, Toyota, and Nissan that were born of cheap oil. Critics said that the auto companies were stupid for putting those gas-guzzlers on the market. But from where I sit it isn't that simple. You hear it said that we don't have an energy policy in America, but in fact we do: cheap oil. That's the federal government's energy policy by default, since it hasn't done anything useful to encourage conservation.

Officials patted themselves on the back for enacting CAFÉ standards in the 1970s. Those regulations, they say, were obviously successful because the industry is meeting them. But wait: the intent of the CAFÉ law was to reduce America's dependence on foreign oil. Thirty years after CAFÉ took effect, we're more dependent than ever. Our energy policy is to encourage the personal use of the automobile as the average American's main method of transportation. The federal government invests in roads, not mass transit. A substantial increase in the gasoline tax 30 years ago would have gone a long way toward solving the problem, but lawmakers couldn't do that—mostly because the government has fixed it so that everybody relies on cheap oil. Politically, it's impossible to make a meaningful change. But you can always pretend, and the best way to do that is to raise CAFÉ standards.

The auto industry is highly leveraged and capital intensive. The Detroit Three have been investing $19 billion annually in research and development (R & D) of new products with enhanced fuel economy and better clean-air performance. That sum, by the way, doesn't include a single screwdriver used by a worker on the assembly line, not to mention the cost of a line of stamping presses or engine manufacturing tools. In recent years, the Big Three domestic automakers have been spending $12–$13 billion per year on new tools and technology. Then, after paying for R & D and capital investment, the companies spend tens of billions of dollars every month to buy parts and services from vendors. These investments support hundreds of thousands of jobs.

So you can see that breakeven points in the auto industry are astronomical. Even when you're going at full capacity in a strong market, you have to work hard basically for 10 or 11 months of the year before you make your first dime. When there's an automotive sales recession, as in 1979 and 2008, it doesn't take much in terms of lost volume to push you into the red, especially when the downturn strikes your most profitable vehicles. In addition to the recession and tough new fuel-economy rules, the auto industry also faced an increasing burden of safety and clean-air regulations in 2008.

Except for a few laughable attempts by the federal government to design a super-efficient automobile for the future, Congress and the White House have done little of solid value to support more fuel-efficient, cleaner cars. We've already talked about the federal government's trade policies, which in essence have given comfort to our enemies. As I've already said, there's a big disconnect between Detroit and Washington in 2008, just as in 1979. There are lots of people in the government who understand banking and international finance. But show me someone in Washington who knows anything about manufacturing . . . then or now. I know, there's a manufacturing "czar" in the Department of Commerce. What he has mostly done is visit plants, collect tokens and other gifts, and put them on display in a showcase in his office.

To complete the round of similarities, the free-market, non-intervention critics who bedeviled Iacocca in 1979 have been reborn in 2008. If anything, there have been so many government bailouts since the Chrysler rescue—savings and loan firms Bear Stearns, Fannie Mae, and Freddie Mac to name a few—that the ideological fervor is just a bit muted.

The main difference between now and then is that in 1979 the Big Three were putting out a bunch of crap. In 2008, quality and design are dramatically better across the domestic fleets, top to bottom. And in manufacturing productivity, as we've seen, the Detroit firms are on a different planet compared with the bad old days. Do I sound like a Big Three booster? If so, I don't apologize. I've worked my ass off for 60 years to understand this business, and I've taken my lumps from the Detroit companies over the years. It's fine to criticize and uphold the ideology of free-market capitalism. But for heaven's sake, let's hear something from the factory floor, where people are getting their hands dirty and applying hard-earned expertise and technical skill to support the American economy.

Nevertheless, you have to understand what went wrong, and here is my list of the 10 worst strategic or tactical decisions by Detroit automakers and the UAW over the past several decades.

1. *The initial denial by the Big Three in the early 1980s that they were uncompetitive in quality, productivity, and cost.* Chrysler's own initial studies of its partner Mitsubishi disclosed a significant production cost difference. This should have been a wake-up call. But Chrysler disregarded the studies, saying it only meant that Mitsubishi had a limited product lineup geared to small cars. Ford also had detailed studies in hand of Mazda, its Japanese partner. These were reinforced by my analysis of Toyota in 1981. Ford also proceeded to do nothing, squandering a chance to lead the Big Three to full competitiveness. GM hadn't even seriously considered itself vulnerable to the Japanese. Its first real glimpse of the future came from my studies. GM could not accept that it wasn't the best. They had forgotten Henry Ford's dictum that "A market is never saturated with a good product, but it is very quickly saturated with a bad one, and no matter how good anything may be when it is first produced, it will not remain good unless its standard is constantly improved."

2. *The UAW's continuous focus on more when Detroit's share of the economic pie was obviously shrinking.* More wages, totally paid healthcare, pensions, vacations, holidays, unrealistic job security programs, all caused hourly payroll costs to skyrocket past $85 per hour. Yes, the auto companies signed those contracts and are equally responsible. I can't fault the union entirely. Generally, the UAW accepted new technology, new methods, and the attrition of active workers. But rich benefits, particularly for hundreds of thousands of retirees, made up a crushing load of legacy costs that pushed many large auto industry parts manufacturing firms into bankruptcy and made it impossible for the Detroit firms to earn healthy profits in a wide-open, hotly competitive U.S. car market.

3. *The 1984 General Motors reorganization.* Up to that year, GM had numerous key operations that were correctly focused on common systems, but were executing badly. There was potential to improve the execution and keep the common focus in design and manufacturing, but GM decided instead on a major corporate tear-up to halt its loss of market share and poor performance in quality and cost. It divided North America into the Chevrolet-Pontiac-Canada (CPC) Group and Buick, Oldsmobile, Cadillac (BOC) Group to work alongside the previously segregated Truck & Bus Group. As a result, GM lost the common focus. Each of the three groups had design, product and manufacturing engineering, assembly, stamping, and powertrain plants, all headed in different directions with unique products and processing. In effect, GM became three competing, non-communicating auto companies. In this inflexible new mode, GM stagnated further.

4. *Chrysler Chairman Lynn Townsend's worldwide expansion strategy that resulted in acquisition of three of the world's weakest automakers.* Unsatisfied with Chrysler's status as an exclusive U.S. domestic automaker, Townsend directed corporate expansions into South Africa, Venezuela,

Argentina, and Australia. Chrysler then bought controlling interests in Rootes Motors in the United Kingdom, Simca Motors in France, and Barriores Diesel in Spain. Chrysler's new international operations—and most significantly Rootes, Simca, and Barriores—recorded huge losses and began a cash drain that helped drive Chrysler toward its federal government bailout.

5. *Too many competing brands.* Another uncompetitive legacy for the Detroit firms was their huge stable of competing brands. The Japanese automakers limited their brands worldwide, and the Big Three were unwilling—or perhaps even unable, given the threat of endless lawsuits from car dealers—to follow that model. Toyota added Lexus® and Scion®; Nissan (originally Datsun) added Infiniti®. Acura® supplemented the Honda marque. Now take GM: It started the 1980s with Chevrolet®, Cadillac®, Buick®, Pontiac®, Oldsmobile® (the one brand it felt confident enough to scrap), GMC®, Opel, and Vauxhall. Then it added Saturn®, Saab®, and Hummer®. Imagine, 11 brands in all! Chrysler had ditched the DeSoto in 1960, but continued with Plymouth®, Dodge®, and Chrysler® brands before buying Jeep® from American Motors. Ford, after canceling the Edsel, was left with the Ford®, Lincoln®, and Mercury® brands. It then added Volvo®, Land Rover®, Jaguar®, and Aston Martin®. The costs of supporting so many brands were considerable in design, product development, manufacturing, sales, and marketing—and remain so.

6. *The Mercedes acquisition of Chrysler.* This deal was billed as a merger of equals, but it actually was part of a worldwide acquisition binge by a small group of German executives who were pressed in the Lynn Townsend mold. There was absolutely no synergy of products, plants, components, or dealers. They were very different types of companies, and refused to reconcile. Mercedes focused on expensive, highly engineered luxury cars and Chrysler was struggling to remain a (more or less) full-line producer of high-volume,

mass-market cars and trucks. Many stockholders and many top executives feathered their nests with this deal. But in the end, it hurt the company and its employees. One has to question what data was presented to Chrysler Corp.'s board of directors to make them go along with this obviously flawed plan.

7. *Ford's acquisition of Volvo, Jaguar, Aston Martin, and Land Rover.* Ford's Lincoln luxury brand didn't do well in international markets, so the company decided to buy its way into the high-profit, premium car market. As one reporter observed, this was a Marx Brothers approach to the car business: if one pie in the face is funny, then 10 pies in the face is 10 times funnier. Adding brands didn't automatically add profit. Investments in engineering, product development, manufacturing, and marketing turned out to be enormous, swallowing the Premier Automotive Group's profit potential and forcing Ford recently to begin unwinding the deals. At this writing, only Lincoln and Volvo remained in its stable.

8. *The clean-sheet approach to product development.* In an all-out effort to leapfrog the Japanese, two companies created products that discarded virtually all existing designs and hardware. GM plowed billions into Saturn, with its totally new car designs, factories, machinery, equipment, tools, processes, workforce, methods, and dealers. One thing worked tolerably well—the new dealer network. Apart from that, the experiment was an utter failure. Saturn still exists, tenuously, in a radically revamped structure. Automakers are willing to tolerate losses in small-car production because those vehicles are essential in helping them meet CAFÉ standards. GM has never said how much it lost on Saturn, but it certainly amounted to many billions of dollars, apparently with minimal contribution to the corporation's fuel-economy ratings. Ford admits to spending $6.5 billion in the 1990s on the Mondeo®, a "world car" that again included an all-new car design, plants, tools, and processes.

The car was successful in Europe, but not in the U.S., and it marked another disastrous failure by a Detroit firm to copy the Toyota global business model.

9. *Excessive focus on trucks and SUVs.* Gas was cheap and big was in, but the Detroit automakers clearly overdid it. With fuel at $1.50 per gallon or less and profits in the big truck segment enormous, the Detroit firms relaxed their focus on small- and mid-sized cars. In 2007, trucks accounted for 61 percent of Chrysler's output, compared with 64 percent at Ford and 53 percent at GM. A more balanced product strategy might have meant somewhat lower profit in strong markets, but also far less damage in years like 2008, with gas prices above $4 per gallon and sales slumping sharply.

10. *The attack on automotive suppliers.* Unable to reduce in-house structural costs quickly enough to compete with Toyota and Honda, the Detroit companies joined in a heavy-handed drive to force huge price cuts from their suppliers of parts, components, and services. They bullied suppliers with threats of contract cancellations, and even were known to take proprietary designs from one supplier and shop them to others. Many suppliers soon ran short on capital and began to go bankrupt or close shop. Once-strong firms that went broke included Dana Corp., Tower Automotive, and Delphi Automotive. These survival dramas also tended to hurt quality.

Now, to balance this out, I'll cite some excellent decisions— things that made a positive difference.

- *Chrysler's acquisition of American Motors.* AMC was first among the Detroit automakers to develop the modern, four-door, mid-sized SUV, a vehicle as influential to this day as the first Chrysler minivan. The Jeep Grand Cherokee®, and the Jeep® brand in general, was the star of that transaction and gave Chrysler a solid core of profitability in the difficult years ahead.

- *The 1994 General Motors reorganization.* Rick Wagoner and his North American strategy team recognized that product development penalties from the 1984 reorganization were dragging the company toward oblivion. So they re-established the Assembly Group, Stamping Group, and Powertrain Group, all with one focus: *common*. GM began to rediscover the benefits of common vehicle platforms, body architectures, plant facilities, tools, processes, and components.

- *The GM-Toyota joint venture at New United Motor Manufacturing, Inc. (NUMMI).* This is the auto industry's supreme example of a win-win-situation in the face of so many failed or mediocre joint ventures. Toyota wanted to ease itself into the U.S. market in a learning environment without excessive investment and exposure to the unknown. GM wanted to learn Toyota's management system.

I'm reminded of the story about Barnie Oldfield, one of the first stars of automobile racing, and Henry Ford. Oldfield and Ford together raced an early Ford car so successfully that both gained dramatically in exposure and reputation. Oldfield became the nation's best-known motorsports figure, and Ford became America's first billionaire. Later in life, the two met and exchanged stories.

"Well Oldfield," Ford said, "I guess we made each other."

"Yes," Oldfield replied. "But I did a hell of a better job of it than you did!"

After nearly 25 years in business, NUMMI is still thriving under Toyota management. Soon after NUMMI shipped its first car, Toyota felt confident enough to begin launching its now-vast North American manufacturing system. GM was able to send numerous executives to experience the Toyota system, but never enough of them to make a big difference in its far-flung global operations. GM, it seems, did a better job teaching Toyota than the reverse!

- *The all-out drive by GM, Ford, and Chrysler to boost quality and productivity.* I've pointed out that Detroit's productivity drive had its ups and downs, and billions of dollars were wasted on false starts. But the fact remains: quality and productivity at the Big Three have improved dramatically as a result of the U.S. auto industry's fierce determination to get competitive.

So you can see that the history of Detroit automakers over the past 30 years has been one of struggle on a difficult path. The Big Three have made plenty of mistakes, offset with massive accomplishments, but there is still considerable unfinished business. I've personally seen in hundreds of factories how Detroit has made progress, but also how they're still beset with lingering structural problems, high legacy costs, a sky-high bill for engineering to government specifications with little government aid, no forgiveness from customers who deserted them because of quality problems, rising competition in North America from Asian and European brands, and a history of governmental indifference to their problems. Today, you can add a new and increasingly severe category of problems: a chronic drain of cash, weak stock prices, negative net worth, negative working capital, historically high levels of debt and a real threat of bankruptcy if the downward spiral isn't reversed—and soon. GM had hoped to hold creditors at bay through 2009, but by the end of 2008, it was nearly out of cash and had to appeal desperately for a federal bridge loan.

GM appeared to be the most vulnerable in mid-2008, which was ironic. From my personal observations, it was ahead of Ford and Chrysler in quality, manufacturing efficiency, and the Three C's. But GM was trapped by its own history. It continued to make high levels of its own parts in-house at uncompetitive labor rates well into the 1990s, and thus had by far the highest retiree pension, healthcare, and job security bill among the Detroit Three.

In 2007, the UAW and the Detroit firms agreed on a pioneering solution to the healthcare cost problem: the Voluntary Employee Beneficiary Association (VEBA). Operated by the union, it would take over funding of blue-collar retiree healthcare benefits after billions of dollars in initial contributions from GM, Ford, and Chrysler. In 2010, as an example, GM must come up with $7 billion to pay into the VEBA. Where will it come from? GM still has too many plants, people, and brands; thus another massive consolidation was in the works at the end of 2008.

Ford was somewhat stronger on its balance sheet, but not much. It had a long way to go to match GM in a "common" approach to the business. Like GM, it suffered from a weak credit rating, high borrowing costs, and heavy debt. There was no realistic end in sight to Ford's chronic unprofitability, although it told Congress it could be back in the black in 2011.

When Daimler-Benz sold it in 2007 and no longer reported financial results, Chrysler became a privately owned company. Chrysler did a creditable job in boosting quality and productivity, but still suffered from its age-old problem: a limited product line and scant resources to fund engineering for massive government regulatory requirements.

Let me say a word or two about the three biggest Japanese automakers operating in the United States. My No. 1 contender to remain strong worldwide always is Honda. The company has driven costs down to a point where it's almost ridiculous to compare it with Detroit. If Ford had to spend $500 million to tool up a plant to produce 400,000 engines a year, Honda maybe would do the same for $180 million. You see these kinds of differences all up and down the production chain at Honda. When a Honda plant decides to replace a stamping press that's making 15 parts per minute, its plant manager tells the tooling supplier: send me one that makes 18 parts per minute. Honda not only engineers quality into the car, but into the manufacturing process.

If you interview for a job today at Honda as an engineer, they only want to know one thing: are you a catalog engineer? In other words, if I have a problem, are you going to look in a catalog for a solution or are you going to sit down and engineer me a solution? If you're a catalog engineer, you don't get hired, because not very much that Honda does comes out of a catalog. They created, designed, and developed what they have, and they want somebody to enhance it. But if you went to almost every company in the United States in the past, everyone you hired, especially in manufacturing, was a catalog engineer. You had a problem with a conveyor? The engineer grabs his parts catalog thinking, *what can I do to solve it?* That's bullshit.

Toyota, plain and simple, is a competitive animal. If you look at the company's most recent financial statements, you can detect some signs of stress because of its blazing worldwide expansion drive. Once the leanest of companies, Toyota now is starting to choke on inventory. It doesn't rely exclusively on in-house engineering for its major production tools like Honda. But it will give an order to a tooling company like this: "Here's the machine tool line I've designed, so don't charge me for any design work, just build it. And you had better make it to my specs, there's no second-guessing me." So, in my mind, Honda and Toyota are on separate planes of existence compared with the rest of the auto manufacturing world.

Nissan is a different kind of company. It has made some mistakes and sort of lost its way in product design and manufacturing efficiency, and fell behind. The company was paralyzed in its keiretsu, or group of interdependent supporting firms. Nobody had the guts to do the hard work needed for a comeback, because those things weren't done in Japan: close plants, cut the workforce, and compete with outsiders on pricing. So Nissan needed a shove from outside, which came in the form of Carlos Ghosn, the executive who took over when it merged with Renault. Ghosn has made a lot of money by kicking people in the ass and saying, "If you can't meet my price, I'm going somewhere else." But Nissan is also basically a very good engineering company. Its assembly plants are somewhat flexible. Nissan doesn't measure up to Honda and Toyota, but I think it has a solid shot at long-term survival.

You never know what the future will bring. Among distinct possibilities is some kind of blockbuster merger involving one or more of the Detroit firms and one or more of the Japanese automakers. But, to say the least, it didn't look very good for GM, Ford, and Chrysler as they pleaded for a sorely needed government loan late in 2008. So the nation faced a decision: *Do we want to keep these companies alive? What was at stake if they failed?*

At the very least, hundreds of thousands of jobs are at stake, as well as the economic health of Michigan, Ohio, Indiana, Illinois, New York, and many other states with significant Big Three operations. But there was an even bigger long-term risk. If the Detroit Three gradually disappeared, Toyota, Honda, Nissan, the Koreans, and the Chinese would eventually fill the gap. Then profits from the American auto industry would largely be sent overseas, and millions of shareholders would go bust. Worse, the foreign companies have kept their major engineering operations at home. If the Big Three fail, America would lose thousands of product engineers, since in all likelihood the foreign companies would continue to do most basic engineering from their home offices. You would still have technical people such as manufacturing engineers for execution of product plans in the foreign-owned American production operations. But do we really want to give up the fundamental skills of automotive design? Wouldn't that make America, at least as far as the auto industry is concerned, a Third-World nation?

Chapter 15

Why We Should Care About Manufacturing

"Making things is important because it brings excitement and joy to the people involved. Human beings are instinctively capable of perceiving beauty in products of high quality and high performance. You must not forget that the act of making things brings joy to your heart and such an act is enjoyable in itself. To exercise your mind, exert your limbs, and spend your time, all for the purpose of making new things, represent a process that you can find gratifying; and when finally the product is complete at the end of your mental and physical exercise, you will be naturally filled with a sense of joy and fulfillment."
—Shoichiro Toyoda, former president,
Toyota Motor Corp.

One of my measures of America's economy isn't very scientific. It's all about Fred Flintstone and Barney Rubble. They were main characters in "The Flintstones," the popular animated TV show that began in the early 1960s. What was so special about them? They were blue-collar guys, just workers eking out a life in a Stone-Age parody of suburbia. What gets me is that everybody could identify with them, because America in the early 1960s had a solid base of blue-collar factory workers.

If you just looked at the auto industry back then, there were entire prosperous towns filled with blue-collar people who went more or less cheerfully to work every day on the assembly line, and expected that their kids would do the same, or at least have the same chance. Detroit, Flint, Pontiac, Saginaw, Dayton, Toledo, Fort Wayne, Kokomo, and Muncie are just a few. The impact on these towns already ranges from devastation to depression, but many more auto-dependent cities could be hurt. Today, how could you have a show based on characters like Fred and Barney? Who would feel empathy? The blue-collar life is fading from America's consciousness, going the way of the dinosaurs.

According to the U.S. Bureau of Labor Statistics, American manufacturing employment stood at 13,501,000 in July of 2008. That was down 29 percent, or about 5.5 million jobs, from July of 1978. Those numbers don't tell the whole story, because they don't include millions of jobs that depend directly on manufacturing—a great deal in mining, for instance—and others in service industries that are indirectly dependent. Of course, part of that job loss is due to higher productivity. The Detroit automobile manufacturers have shed hundreds of thousands of jobs in the name of efficiency. And, I've already said that every job added at the Japanese automotive operations in the U.S. cuts Detroit employment by more than one job. In the beginning, the domestic automakers (and their suppliers) lost three jobs for every one added at the transplants.

A great deal of job loss is also due to loss of market share by American manufacturers. In the first seven months of 2008, vehicles built overseas accounted for 26 percent of all new car and truck sales in the United States. Foreign companies manufacturing vehicles in the U.S. continue to sell vast numbers of cars and trucks here that were built in the assembly operations of their home countries. Detroit automakers export very few vehicles, as we've seen.

There's currently a strong debate in America about whether or not the middle class is disappearing, and whether this is good or bad for us. There are probably respectable arguments on both sides, but one statistic stands out for me: inequality of income. For decades, the U.S. Bureau of Census has compiled data on what it calls the general income inequality (GINI) scale. The scale runs from zero to one. Zero represents perfect equality—everybody in America has the same amount of money. One, at the top of the scale, is perfect inequality—one individual has all the wealth. America has been steadily moving up that scale. For 2007, the GINI ratio was 0.463, compared to 0.397 in 1967. In other words, there has been a 17 percent increase in income inequality in America in that time frame, according to the Census Bureau.

The rich are definitely getting richer. And if you ask me, the main problem here is that America lost its focus on manufacturing, because manufacturing jobs historically are among the highest paid. In Detroit, we don't need the Census Bureau to tell us this. Practically every day some automaker or parts supplier kicks people out the door or cuts their wages and benefits. My sense of all this is not just that we were overtaken in manufacturing, but that we lost our belief in the factory life. We seem to think that service and financial businesses will maintain our standard of living. So what if we let people in China do the grimy factory work, people say, that frees us to focus on innovation and other futuristic pursuits. Today, Fred and Barney would be janitors or stock boys at Wal-Mart.

I can't help thinking about my father, the tool and die maker, who took considerable pride in being a productive man whose job made a difference in the world. In peak years he worked 10 hours per day, six or seven days per week, and earned enough to support a family well—until his early death at age 60. Today, he would have trouble finding a job in the U.S. because much of the tool and die construction business has gone overseas.

In the auto industry, the Detroit manufacturers have refocused in recent years on several core items. They make vehicle bodies, engines, and automatic transmissions, and progressively less of anything else. Many of the components they once made in-house, including castings, forgings, seats, bearings, bumpers, instrument panels, and numerous other items, have been given to competent North American suppliers. But a great deal of that work also has gone overseas. Select engines and transmissions are made in Japan or Europe for use in Detroit-designed vehicles. As the use of electronics and electrical equipment increases in American-made automobiles, so does the proportion of that stuff built overseas.

I know for a fact that much of this outsourcing would stop if our highly paid CEOs would concentrate on boosting the quality, productivity, and cost performance of their own plants instead of closing or selling them. But that's hard, and selling out is easy. Perhaps members of the boards of directors of these corporations should make CEO pay depend at least in part on productivity and quality, instead of allowing top executives to collect huge bonuses simply by bailing out. For instance, I watched Mercedes buy Freightliner, one of the largest U.S. manufacturers of medium- and heavy-duty trucks. There was absolutely nothing Mercedes could do to make Freightliner more competitive that the company's American management couldn't have done just as well. Then Mercedes bought Chrysler Corp., a profitable company that became a basket case that finally had to be sold to a hedge fund for a fraction of its purchase cost. Chrysler's board of directors had to be completely unconscious when this plan was pushed through; a blind man could have seen there would be no synergy because again, Mercedes had nothing to offer except ownership. In both cases, Freightliner and Chrysler, I believe the motivation was clear: the personal enrichment of CEOs. And I believe a new truism is emerging: productivity is a better long-term strategy for most American businesses than selling out.

I think Dr. Toyoda (as he was universally known) was right. People make things because they like to do it. I've been around factory people all my life. They can be coarse and demanding, but also passionate about what they're doing. Where do you find this passion today? It's in Japan, of course. There, the question of whether they should care about manufacturing never comes up. The same is true in Korea and throughout Europe. And watch out for China. According to the National Association of Manufacturers, if China can continue boosting its manufacturing output by 10 percent a year as it has done for several past years, it will equal America's factory output by 2020. In 2008, it will only produce about 60 percent of America's output, according to NAM. Now, if China uses some of its wealth to consume American-made goods—in other words, if it opens up its doors to two-way trade—then its growth is a good thing. If, however, it continues to export billions of dollars worth of goods to the U.S. while refusing to foster imports, that's bad, according to NAM. My guess is that

China will take the latter course, mostly because that worked so well for Japan and Korea. So don't ask China whether it's a good strategy to focus on manufacturing.

Here's a challenge: go to your neighborhood sporting goods store or discount retailer and try to find something that was made in America. We import high-line shoes, athletic shoes, underwear, suits, dresses, toys—why even bother to list them? Just as remarkably, we continue to send manufacturing operations overseas. Boeing right now is developing a new commercial airliner, the 787. Major parts of the body and the wings will be made in Japan. Our brilliant military is considering sourcing the design of a new U.S. Air Force tanker aircraft to Europe's Airbus, with assembly only in Alabama.

Fortunately in America, there are still many large globally competitive companies that consider efficient manufacturing a strategic necessity. I'll just name a few: Intel, John Deere, Manitowoc, Caterpillar, and General Electric (GE).

A true manufacturing conglomerate, GE has stakes in numerous businesses. Its strategic plan is to be the No. 1 or No. 2 company in a specific product line by focusing on competitive manufacturing, or else get out. For decades, General Motors was a major manufacturer of railroad locomotives in the U.S., and the business was profitable. Its major competitor, GE eventually overtook GM in production and sales. GE had established a plan to address quality, productivity and cost, and invested heavily in new technology. GM discovered its locomotive business was no longer a cash cow, decided that one-million-pound railroad vehicles didn't fit its portfolio, and sold the business to a private investment group. Today, GE is the premier North American manufacturer of locomotives. The same process has made GE top dog in the production of airplane engines. The company was under intense pressure from the airlines for more fuel-efficient, quieter engines. That caused GE to re-evaluate its entire engine design and manufacturing processes, involving a detailed analysis of its:

- product portfolio and technology,
- manufacturing operations and technology,

- quality systems,
- productivity focus,
- cost structure, and
- competitors' strengths and weaknesses.

Results have been just as dramatic as in GE's locomotive business. Rolls-Royce and Pratt-Whitney, two other major aircraft engine manufacturers, now are facing formidable competition from GE.

On the other hand, GE now is reportedly planning the sale of its home appliance businesses. Obviously there are billions of dollars to pocket from the sale, but the market for washers, dryers, dishwashers, and other items is rapidly changing. GE was able to hold foreign competitors at bay for years with a stern determination to keep quality, productivity, and cost under control. Today, a typical GE clothes dryer lists at a price that's not dramatically higher than its 1965 model—what if GM or Ford could say the same? But the crush of new competitors has made it difficult for GE to remain No. 1 or No. 2. Will the new owners of this business, whoever they are, keep the manufacturing plants in the U.S. or move them overseas?

Boeing is also embarking on a major restructuring of products and manufacturing focus with introduction of its 787 commercial jet. In the past, Boeing was known for making all the major body and wing assemblies for its aircraft, while buying some major systems from suppliers, such as engines and landing gear. But with the 787, several Japanese companies including Kawasaki and Mitsubishi are producing the wings and two-thirds of the fuselage. In effect, Boeing is restructuring to be a designer and assembler of airplanes, while shedding major manufacturing operations. And how long will it be until Boeing and Airbus both are facing new competition in the Far East?

Caterpillar and John Deere are prime examples of American companies that have decided not to retreat in the face of tough global competition.

Deere has a fabulously extensive product line: farm tractors in various sizes, combines, harvesters, chemical sprayers, planters, logging equipment, lawn mowers, and so forth. A key element of its strategic plan was to enlist its entire workforce—50,000 people—in a drive to enhance quality, productivity, and manufacturing processes. Deere has seen a steady improvement in worldwide sales. It has been opening factories instead of closing them, hiring workers instead of booting them out the door.

Caterpillar is another first-class act. The company has $45 billion in annual sales to the construction, landscaping, mining, paving, and pipeline businesses. Caterpillar makes diesel engines to fit its products as well as for ships, trucks, off-road vehicles, and power generation. Only 37 percent of its sales are in the United States. The company was only marginally competitive when it faced a formidable threat from Komatsu of Japan. Komatsu had a complete line of products, with high quality and attractive pricing. Caterpillar had the three classic choices: sit back, do nothing, and hope for the best; sell the business; or start a process to make the company competitive in product offerings, quality, productivity, and manufacturing cost. Obviously it chose the latter, thanks to a management team and board of directors who believed in a "common" approach to manufacturing and sensible use of new technology.

Famously, Caterpillar also decided to challenge the UAW—something that hasn't happened among the Detroit-based automakers. In one of the longest and most contentious American labor disputes of the 1990s, Caterpillar endured two strikes while forcing the union to accept more efficient plant-level working agreements. The union essentially surrendered after thousands of its own workers crossed the picket lines, helping the company rack up strong sales and profits in the middle of the battle.

Caterpillar has achieved dramatic gains in quality, productivity and even job safety. Work has been simplified and waste eliminated. Today, the company touts the Caterpillar Production System as fervently as Toyota does its own. In 2007, "Cat" recorded its fifth straight year of record sales and fourth straight year of record profit.

Now here's something you can cut out and hang on your bulletin board if you run a manufacturing company, large or small. I've spent nearly 60 years thinking about the factory floor, and here's how I believe it should be run.

- *Focus on today's technology before buying something new.* Chances are you can make the older equipment work well enough to meet your need for continuous improvement. I've seen hundreds of examples of this, but none better than Capsugel, my first big consulting job with Harbour & Associates. Remember, it was considering a $150 million investment in new technology to replace under-performing gelatin capsule manufacturing machines whose design dated to about 1916. Today, the output of these machines has been multiplied by about 300 percent since 1982, thanks to technical modifications and new quality processes.

- *When possible, never do "all new."* There are always exceptions. Sometimes technological change is so great that nothing less will work, such as the use of new composite materials in airplane construction. But it should never be done for its own sake. Automakers have tried many times to do "all new" with such famous results as the Edsel and the Chevrolet Vega. The Saturn® car is another case. It included an all-new car, several new plants, new technology, new tooling, and a new way of managing the workforce. This kind of approach is guaranteed to create more problems than can be reasonably handled. As I've said, you'll never see Toyota or Honda doing it.

I think the world loves "all new" because that phrase has been used in just about every advertising campaign in the past 75 years. The world loves it: all-new cars, airplanes, and computers; the list is endless. Nobody likes "all new" better than the Pentagon. Just look at the U.S. Air Force F22 Raptor fighter jet with its delivery price before development costs of $138,000,000 (yes, that's millions). That's $16.8 billion for the 122 planes already delivered. Just imagine. That sum would buy 675,000 mid-sized cars. As I understand it, the F22 total program cost is $62.5 billion or approximately $250 million per airplane counting development costs. This all-new, totally unique plane started in development in 1992 and wasn't completed until 2002. So we're willing to bill the taxpayers $62.5 billion for a couple hundred aircraft. This is absolutely frightening: all-new fuselage, wings, landing gear, engines, avionics, and weapons systems. It's insane. Was there just no way that an existing plane could have been modified to incorporate the new technology? Did we really have to start at zero on the learning curve for design, product and manufacturing engineering, and sourcing from suppliers? The military obviously lives in a different world, unaware that the auto industry has learned the hard way to keep away from "all new."

- *Pay attention to detail. Don't assume.* Management staff frequently takes it for granted that workers will carry out assignments, even without rigid discipline. But something will always slip. A follow-up system is necessary—for everything. I learned from a U.S. Marine Corps drill sergeant that every directive must be religiously followed up, from making up your bunk correctly to getting a haircut regularly. In the auto industry, it used to be normal to take three months or more to get an assembly line up to full speed on a new product. This was mostly because plant management didn't insist on a more disciplined approach. Discipline means getting it right on time. This is why Honda likes auto racing: it builds team discipline. You can't win the race if you don't show up at the start gate with everything ready.

- *Adopt a "common" focus.* My prime example of the wrong way to meet a quality and productivity challenge is the 1984 GM reorganization. It created two car groups, each one focused on unique products, engineering, tooling, and processing. Billions of dollars were wasted in duplicate tooling investment and engineering cost. Quality and productivity got worse. The two-division structure was abandoned in 1994, and GM has just recently begun to gain benefits from its rededication to the three C's: *common, common, common*. In effect, 15 years or more were lost and GM had nothing to halt the rapid increase in U.S. market share by Japanese automakers.

- *Be extremely wary of expanding by acquisitions.* I saw first-hand how Chrysler's purchase of failing auto companies in Europe drove it to the brink of insolvency and forced it to beg for a government loan guarantee. When you're conducting your due diligence review of a company you want to buy—whether it's a billion-dollar parts supplier or a small shop down the street making washers—send your best manufacturing people to scour the operation and gauge its true value and potential.

- *Think twice before reorganizing your shop to make it more competitive.* If your competitors are gaining on you, make certain you've done everything possible to improve basic productivity and quality before you disrupt the flow of the plant.

- *Lean manufacturing is not the total solution.* Many corporate CEOs and manufacturing executives are embracing lean as the ultimate solution to massive improvements in quality, productivity, and cost. The lean ethic, while absolutely necessary, will only take you so far. Don't forget the front end! *Designers and product engineers are the direct source of 85 percent of the total cost of a product or component.* Their designs also substantially affect product quality and reliability. Responsible management must focus on the design and product engineering staffs, demanding continuous improvement in quality, productivity, reliability, and the reduction of complexity.

I don't know if I have a final, all-encompassing recommendation. Manufacturing today has gone back to simple principles. *Keep it lean; keep it flowing. Never stop; and don't chase magic bullets.* That's a solid formula for success in the factory, but somehow it doesn't seem like a big enough statement to mark the end of an era.

As the world plunges into economic crisis, some people were predicting the end of America's dominance in global finance. Sadly, we've already seen the end of America's pre-eminence in auto manufacturing. I'm sure I've lived much too long. I'm five years past the normal male life expectancy, and it's hard for me to accept that American manufacturing and, in particular, the three Detroit auto companies, got into such a mess that they had to go to Washington to beg for a bailout. If you read this far you know how and why it happened. They pushed manufacturing into the background as a necessary corporate discipline. They failed in quality, productivity, and customer care. They couldn't match a made-in-Japan business model with intrinsic advantages that focused on low-cost, high-quality designs. And their government followed a decades-long trade policy that tended to favor and protect Detroit's competitors. But more than this is involved, and I'd like to say just a few final words about the Big Three. Each story is different.

Chrysler was the industry's most profitable company when Chairman Lee A. Iacocca bypassed Bob Lutz, who was Chrysler's president and the industry's most able executive, and named Bob Eaton as his successor. I was stunned to see Eaton, a former GM product engineer, take over the company. He proceeded to run Chrysler as if it were GM. He made huge investments in engines, automatic transmissions, and other technologies that drove manufacturing costs out of sight. Then he fostered the sale of the company to Mercedes, keeping Lutz completely out of those negotiations. I knew Mercedes well. It was an extremely high cost, high price, specialty manufacturer that got lost in the jungle of managing a car company that sold 3 million vehicles a year to a mass market. The wreckage that we see today—a shrinking hourly and salaried workforce and shattered dealer body—was the direct result. Eaton made out okay, however, along with a select group of executives who used the comically misnamed "merger of equals" to line their pockets.

Ford today should be on top of the automotive world. Remember, in 1980 I was shown internal studies that itemized the company's cost disadvantage against its Japanese partner Mazda, which came to roughly the same conclusion as my own concurrent study of Toyota. Forewarned, Ford had a golden opportunity to put a strategic plan in place to get competitive—at least as far as the things that were within the company's control. After all, that was the company's inheritance from its founder, Henry Ford, whom we've quoted here because his words still ring true. But what did Ford do? The company hacked away at the problem here and there, but in comprehensive terms, it did absolutely nothing. After multiple CEOs, each promising a turnaround, the company languishes in the sewer with a tarnished blue oval.

General Motors would have been in bankruptcy court long ago except for one man—CEO Rick Wagoner and his team of executives. Their drive for the three C's, starting in 1994, helped to reverse a corporate death spiral that began with the disastrous 1984 reorganization under Chairman Roger B. Smith and President F. James McDonald. As I've said, that blunder set GM back 15 years and contributed to the decline in market share and profitability that left it dangerously weak.

There's only one conclusion: each of the Detroit manufacturers opened the door for Toyota, Honda, and Nissan.

But I'm not done yet. My biggest problem is that I'm disgusted with many of today's CEOs. It seems their principal focus is to line their pockets with enormous salaries, pensions, and golden parachutes. I've seen this before. I personally watched former Chrysler Chairman Lynn Townsend buy worthless companies in wonderful countries—so that he could go quail hunting in Spain, attend the theatre in London, and dine at legendary restaurants in Paris. Then there's Chrysler CEO Bob Nardelli, who drained Home Depot's cash drawer as he was shown the door and, at this writing, was negotiating what could be the end of Chrysler as a corporate entity.

I suspect some of you are reading this skeptically, but *no*, I'm not one of America's multi-millionaires. The one thing I cherish most in life is integrity, a moral and ethical concept I've always tried to follow. It is a word that many of today's CEOs apparently don't know how to spell. The drive for self-gratification, to close this book with a word that I used to open it, is bullshit. Imagine how different America's economic situation would be today if ethics and honor had ruled the executive suites!

Epilogue

I have to admit it. I felt sad, angry, and a little bit sick to my stomach as I watched top executives of GM, Ford, and Chrysler appear before Congress in November of 2008 asking for a financial rescue. It was 1979 all over again, including the deafening sound of minds snapping shut like steel traps all over Washington, D.C. (as one executive described it during the first Chrysler bailout). Hell, the cheap shot artists in the Capitol even reprised the flap about auto executives flying around on corporate jets, reminiscent of the day that Steve Miller and I had to scrape Lee A. Iacocca off the ceiling 30 years earlier. How many times have we read about members of Congress hitching rides on corporate jets for their overseas fact-finding junkets? And the final indignity: the Big Three were spanked soundly and sent back home to draw up plans proving they wouldn't squander their requested $25 billion in bridge loans that would prevent them from going into bankruptcy: just like prep school students forced to write a 1,000-word essay on why they shouldn't play hooky. Their latest request has increased the $25 billion to $34 billion to starve off bankruptcy. The $25 billion referenced here is the amount Congress approved in 2007 to help build fuel-efficient cars, which is distinct from the bridge loans they are looking for at the end of 2008.

Life is definitely not fair. Here were three American companies that had spent hundreds of billions of dollars since 1980 on factories, tools, and equipment—real money that had provided untold numbers of jobs across the nation and made them world-competitive in sheer factory productivity and quality. And hundreds of billions more was spent on purchasing, marketing, and salaries. Add it all up and it vastly exceeds the $750 billion that the government created to buy up the euphemistically named "troubled assets" held by banks.

The treatment the automakers received in Washington was shabby in the extreme; and all the while, the federal government was doling out piles of borrowed cash to financial companies that had irresponsibly created phony financial structures that, predictably and necessarily, collapsed in a heap. And, if anyone complained about the corporate jets at AIG, Citigroup, J. P. Morgan, and the other banks, I never heard about it. (Okay, there were a few gripes about off-site meetings at vacation spots.) Did AIG submit a public plan to get $150 billion? No way! What about spending plans from Fanny Mae, Ginny Mac, J. P. Morgan, and Citigroup? Meanwhile, the federal government was doling out billions of dollars in largesse, without even revealing the names of the recipients, much less holding their feet to the fire.

In short, American manufacturing can wilt slowly on the vine as far as the federal government is concerned. But if the banking or investment community is threatened, it snaps immediately into action. We've seen this before. In the 1979–1981 recession, the Federal Reserve kept interest rates high to fight inflation caused by high oil prices. The factory economy was pushed in many cases to the brink of extinction. But when the banks began to show signs of stress, the Federal Reserve backed off and let money flow easier.

In the context of America's economic crash of 2008, $25 billion in loan guarantees to the Detroit automakers looked like a pittance. For years now, the steady deterioration of balance sheets at GM, Ford, and Chrysler has been apparent to anyone who bothered to look at the numbers. Lenders could have foreclosed on GM well before the company conceded it needed a financial rescue, but the theory was that GM and Ford were too big to fail. That idea was being tested as 2008 drew to a close.

Shall we recap? It was Congress that failed to deliver an energy policy to reduce America's addiction to oil; and Congress that left America extremely vulnerable to wide swings in oil pricing that resulted in crude approaching $150 per barrel, gasoline prices above $4 per gallon, and diesel prices closing in on $5 per gallon (and I'd like to know: how many people defaulted on mortgages because of high energy prices that busted their household budgets?).

And here were members of Congress blaming the Big Three for building big cars and trucks instead of looking inwardly. Again, it was Congress that mandated ever stricter and more costly fuel economy, safety, and environmental regulations while Detroit's ability to fund them was evaporating. And why was cash flow at the Detroit companies lagging while these mandates were piled on? In part, at least, because the federal government had written the rules of global trade, and some of the auto industry regulations to favor Detroit's foreign-based competitors.

We've talked about how American trade policy is essentially a bribe to keep our trading partners aligned with our political outlook, while in other nations trade policy is designed to favor business and the middle class. They can sell to us, but we can't sell to them. It will be supremely ironic if the Detroit automakers succeed in getting a federal loan guarantee, and then are hauled into court by the World Trade Organization for getting government subsidies. Imagine the European and Asian automakers subsidized and coddled to the hilt by their governments, whining about a loan to the Big Three that must be repaid with interest!

And look at the unequal treatment on the regulatory front. For instance, Japanese companies always found it easier to comply with Corporate Average Fuel Economy (CAFÉ) regulations, even when they were getting heavily into the gas-guzzler game. This is because the days when they mainly produced small cars had given them tons of CAFÉ credits that they could use in the future to offset any shortfalls in their fleet's average fuel economy ratings. And look at Europe: Mercedes, BMW, and Porsche flatly refused to build the kind of cars that the U.S. government wanted. They decided their best strategy was to ignore the standards and pay annual fines, and they were probably right. At least no one has come forward to blame them.

Indeed, one of the major rules in Washington is that foreign automakers are allowed to run and hide when the blame game begins. The Detroit companies were whipped for building big pickup trucks, sport utility vehicles (SUVs), and full-sized cars, but nobody said anything about Toyota and Nissan doing exactly the same. The reality is that automakers build what customers want. And, when energy policy dictates cheap gasoline, Americans will continue to see big and powerful vehicles as their birthright. As of this writing, gasoline had fallen well under $2 per gallon, and current energy policy from Washington offered nothing substantial, like a gasoline tax, to encourage conservation.

CAFÉ legislation is a proven failure: fleet average fuel economy improves, but people drive more. The focus of the original CAFÉ law was to reduce dependence on foreign oil; under 30 years of CAFÉ, we're more dependent than ever. And the insanity continues. Now Congress has decreed an increase in the fuel economy fleet requirement from 27.5 to 35 miles per gallon. That stroke of the legislative pen will require an investment of at least $80 billion to retool assembly, engine, and transmission plants—all to build vehicles that customers might not want.

Further, it was Congress and the White House that allowed the mortgage-based financial bubble to build and then collapse, resulting in a credit freeze that sent car and truck sales tumbling to their lowest level in a generation. While Congress dragged its feet on an auto industry bailout, new product development in Detroit had all but halted. That's more comfort, courtesy of Congress, to Detroit's foreign rivals in an industry where you can't afford to fall behind. We have to blame both ends of the political spectrum: those on the right, who stand up tall for the ideology that the government shouldn't intervene in the market (as long as it doesn't hurt their home state, anyway) and those on the left who seem to want to operate GM as a public utility that only builds the kind of vehicles that the government tells them to build. Indeed, life is not fair.

Average Americans don't need to know much about the intricacies of manufacturing and world trade. They just want to see attractive, high-quality, high-value cars when they go to the local dealership. But it is inexcusable for America's leaders to show such shocking ignorance about the factory life. They take the easy way out: if Detroit is in a mess, it's because of lazy, stupid, greedy management.

I know what junk the Detroit Three were shipping in the 1970s and 1980s, but I've also seen their strong revival in quality and productivity. I also grant you that the UAW has fought for a wide range of benefits that put the Detroit firms at a competitive disadvantage: free healthcare for retirees, generous pensions, job-security plans, and inefficient plant-level work rules. But when these came under fire in Washington, it was hard not to think how Congress has paid itself, its staffers, and legions of government workers a similar range of lavish benefits above the reach of most Americans. But when you look at the depth of the financial trouble at the Big Three—GM sitting there, for instance, with about $50 billion in negative net worth—you can only go along with what Iacocca said once under similar circumstances: "Nobody is *that* stupid."

Watching the auto industry hearings before Congress, the thing that really infuriated me was the total lack of appreciation of what was at stake. Here's what our elected officials in Washington were risking in their game of liquidation roulette (because, in all practicality, bankruptcy for the automakers probably would amount to exiting the business rather than reorganization and revival):

- Europe, Japan, and Korea, where manufacturing is considered a national advantage, will dominate the North American market.

- China would become a far stronger, major competitor here.

- Most, if not all, product development will take place overseas; engineering students in American universities will have to go there to find jobs.

- A majority of major capital investments, such as stamping press lines, body shops, and engine and transmission manufacturing tools, will go to foreign companies.

- Foreign manufacturers will expand in southern right-to-work states. They wouldn't buy most of the defunct GM, Ford, or Chrysler plants in the industrial Midwest. It would take years for the foreigners to expand their production base here, creating a supply vacuum that likely would be filled with increasing numbers of vehicles imported from overseas.

- Vehicle prices would rise because of diminished competition.

- In the debate over a Detroit rescue, little attention was given to the real possibility that Detroit would recover and repay whatever the automakers received in government loans. The U.S. Treasury might even make a profit on the deal as it had in the first Chrysler bailout.

- Historically, the Detroit firms have been major contributors to charities and foundations. A notable example was in the wake of the September 11, 2001 attack on America. Ford, GM, and DaimlerChrysler each contributed $10 million to the Red Cross and other forms of victim support. Most of their foreign competitors gave nothing. And GM offered its "Get America Moving" marketing blitz that sparked vehicle sales by offering employee-pricing incentives. Ford and DaimlerChrysler followed suit.

This drama was still being played out as of this writing. But it was clear that the face of America's auto industry would again change dramatically. The UAW had begun another round of bargaining to give back some of its cherished benefits. According to newspaper reports, the union may finally have been frightened into canceling the Jobs Bank, the income security program that paid workers for not working. And blockbuster mergers were still possible, despite the collapse of merger discussions between GM and Chrysler.

America's face is changing too. You can see it in the smallest things. I went to the dentist the other day for my semi-annual checkup and cleaning. The hygienists were brainstorming on how to get more customers. Auto industry workers and retirees used to patronize them freely, since their dental plans paid for everything. But that was rapidly drying up. People wouldn't pay to have their teeth cleaned; they wouldn't visit the dentist unless something hurt. How many hygienists would lose their jobs, for goodness sake?

What America needs most right now is a good jolt of the power of the factory. This goes far beyond the troubles of the domestic auto industry, which is just a victim of this nation's loss of faith in the manufacturing way of life. I've talked about how GM, Ford, and Chrysler, obsessed by the fashion of the latest model change, lost the sense that quality and productivity were their top priorities. Maybe it's no surprise after all that the government and Wall Street adopted the same attitude. I've also shown how the Detroit automakers revived the century-old heritage of Henry Ford and the other pioneers of auto production, slowly and painfully in the 1980s and 1990s regaining full competitiveness on the factory floor. But it was too late, perhaps. As a result, fewer Americans today have the same chance that I had: the son of a tool and die maker who gladly followed his father into the factory and made a good life there.

Even as our wealth as a nation disappears, and the ranks of the middle class thin, I'm still frightened (panicked would be a better word) that executives of American manufacturing firms will continue to source jobs offshore, further destroying our industrial base and the comfortable livelihoods it provides. It's happening, in part, because that's a handy short-term solution to the new world of global competition. Many of our top executives look only at the lowest-price quote when making a decision on whether to build something in-house, buy it from a domestic parts supplier, or import it from the latest low-wage venue. Major sections of Boeing's upcoming Dreamliner® aircraft will be made in Japan and Italy. Chrysler is preparing to import small cars from China, and GM makes a small car in Korea. Televisions are practically all imported. And so on.

As a people, we still have a knack for making things. What would the U.S. auto market look like today if GM, Ford, and Chrysler had mounted all-out quality and productivity drives in the 1970s? That's what General Electric did, and it held the worldwide competition at bay for decades in the home appliance business. We have numerous national role models for manufacturing, in fact. Caterpillar remains among the best and healthiest in the world in heavy equipment production as a result of its focus on manufacturing. Harley-Davidson thrives today because it completely revamped its manufacturing systems in the 1980s, bringing quality and productivity up to world-class levels. Warner-Lambert discovered in the early 1980s that a renewed focus on quality and productivity can transform a troubled company. Its Capsugel subsidiary, which makes gelatin capsules for the pharmaceutical industry, is now a profitable, vibrant concern that regularly beats the competition, thanks to productivity gains in the range of 300 percent. There are also new companies on the leading edge of economic innovation. Intel, for instance, is every bit as strong in quality and productivity as the microchips it makes to power so many of the world's computers. This has to be our future as a nation—to get back to making things better and more efficiently than anybody else, and thus to rebuild our standard of living.

Just think. In time, the North American auto market will recover and even resume growth. But the main beneficiaries will be foreign-owned companies whose focus is on manufacturing, unless we work to prevent it.